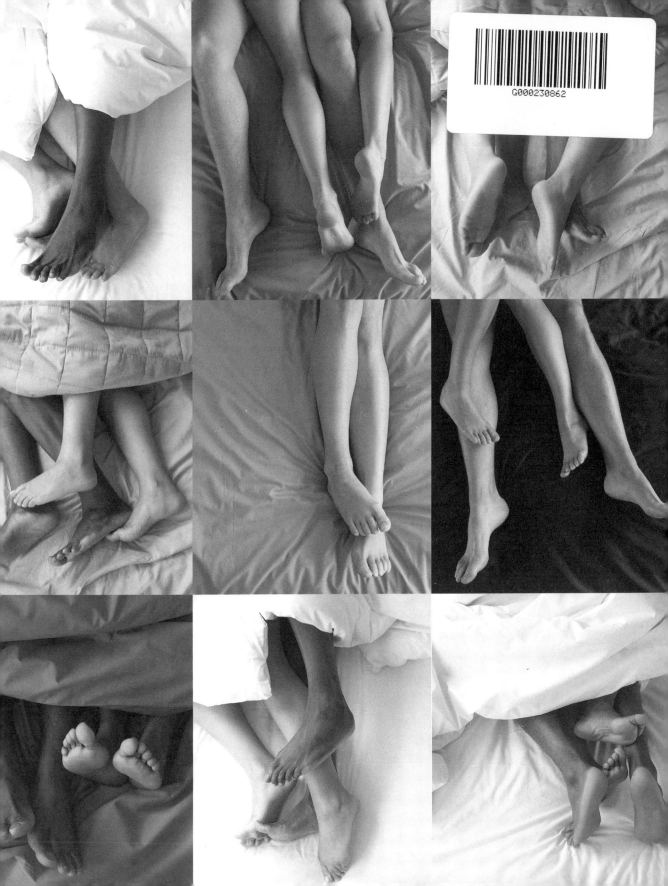

Tracey Cox
supersex
for life

the great sex guide
for long-term lovers

London, New York, Munich, Melbourne, Delhi

Project Editor Laura Palosuo
Senior Art Editor Helen Spencer
Executive Managing Editor Adèle Hayward
Managing Art Editor Kat Mead
Production Editor Maria Elia
Senior Production Editor Jennifer Murray
Senior Production Controller Man Fai Lau
Art Director Peter Luff
Publisher Stephanie Jackson

Produced for Dorling Kindersley by:
Editor Dawn Bates
Design SEA

First published in Great Britain in 2010 by
Dorling Kindersley Limited
80 Strand, London WC2R 0RL
A Penguin Company

2 4 6 8 10 9 7 5 3 1

A CIP catalogue of this book is available from
the British Library.

ISBN 978-1-4053-4459-3
Printed in Singapore by Star Standard

See our complete catalogue at **www.dk.com**

Contents

Introduction

Is it possible to stay in love and have good, regular, lusty sex long term?

It's the question everyone ponders but no one appears to have the answer to. We've only really just started talking openly and honestly about sex – or more accurately the lack of it – in long-term relationships. And it's not a comfortable discussion. It's a rare couple that are happily shagging away 10 years in – but why? Most of us go into a relationship loved-up, clued-up, and determined to be the couple that are the exception to the rule. Ten years on, we're as bored, indifferent, or contemptuous as the parents we vowed we'd never turn into. Why are best intentions not good enough? Why does the person we desperately lust after at the start always seem to morph into a "best friend" we want to cuddle but no longer crave sexually? Is having great sex long term a myth as tenuous and nonsensical as the tooth fairy? And if it is possible and achievable, where and why are we all going so horribly wrong?

This book is my take on this age-old problem. It offers both fact and opinion on why sex seems to have an even lower survival rate than long-term love, along with workable, practical solutions that, I believe, could make you the couple everyone else envies. Based on the latest scientific developments and theories from the world's best-regarded therapists, the result (I hope!) is a necessarily brutal, honest look at society's oldest and biggest relationship problem. But one that isn't too heavy or judgemental – and will make you giggle as well as groan. Unlike my other books, you need to read this one in order because each stage works on what you learnt from the last. For the sake of simplicity, when I refer to "marriage" I mean any long-term monogamous relationship and although I use "him" and "her", the advice is equally as useful for gay couples as it is straight. While the book is obviously aimed at long-term couples, it's also wise reading for those (lucky, lucky bastards) who are still in the first, fabulous flushes of love to best prepare for what's ahead. I hope you all find it as helpful as I very much hope it will be.

1
So
How's
Your
Sex
Life?

How
Is It
for You?

How do you stack up against the average? Are you really a victim of boring bed syndrome – or suffering from unrealistic sexpectations? Find out what's normal, what's not – and the surprising truths the real statistics reveal.

This feature kicks off the book because it's all about challenging myths. You want to improve your sex life? Fantastic! But let's make sure that what you're aiming for is both realistic and possible. And let's arm you with some stats on what really happens with sex long term, rather than have you labouring under the misapprehension that *every* other couple but you two is out there having stupendously spectacular, effortless sex five times a day (and 10 times at the weekend).

So you're about to get a reality check – one that I suspect and hope will make you feel a whole lot better about your own situation. It may not be as dire or hopeless as you think. There's a perverse pleasure in realizing the rest of the world is just as screwed up (or more) as we are and immense reassurance in knowing that what we're grappling with are problems *everyone* struggles with.

Now, before we get stuck in, a word about the sex statistics you'll read on page 16. Lots of studies about sex and relationships (indeed studies on anything) vary wildly because of the differences in assessment methods and the people studied. Some studies and sources are infinitely more reputable than others, and I've tried to base most of the statistics here on those. But, even then, use them as a point of interest and broad comparison rather than something to be measured up to. (Christ, the last thing I want to do is give you *more* standards to live up to!) First though, let's start by looking at some of the reasons people may have told you your sex life isn't up to par and sort out fact from fiction. There are some silly, *silly* sex myths out there and this will hopefully lay the most common to rest. Ahem.

Sex offers us many things, not just erotic release. It's also about love, fun and – crucially – connection to your partner.

Nine signs you don't have problems

01 You're still having solo sex

Assuming you aren't replacing sex with each other with masturbation, this is a plus not a problem! It doesn't mean you're not getting enough sex or that it's unsatisfactory. It simply means you may feel like a bit when your partner's either not there or not interested. Solo sex is selfish, usually based on a filthy fantasy you don't particularly want to share, and accomplished in under five minutes. It's effortless and a little something to perk up an otherwise dull day. It's a side dish to the main course sex you have with your partner but also has spin-off benefits for them. Studies repeatedly show that people who masturbate regularly have higher libidos. It isn't clear what came first, the chicken or the egg: does putting our hands down our pants cause us to want more sex or do we want more sex generally and that's why we have our hands down our pants? Doesn't really matter though. As one greeting card put it: "Life is short: fiddle with your willy while you can".

02 You don't have sex often

First, check the stats (see page 16) to see if this is indeed true, then look at where you're at in your relationship. The averages of how often couples have sex are just that: averages. All couples have dips and peaks depending on the stage of their relationship. If you're having sex once a month and have only been together for six, it could be a problem. If you've got two kids under five, both work full time, and have financial problems, it would be bizarre if you *were* swinging from the chandeliers every night. It's normal for sex to take a back seat at certain stages: frequency is an indicator of sex problems but not an absolute. How is the quality? Lots of couple prefer to have a longish sex session once a fortnight than three quick sessions. How high is your sex drive? If you both have quite low libidos, having sex once a month might be perfect for both of you.

03 You fantasize during sex

Pretty much all of us are guilty of this and it means nothing. However desperately you love your partner, it won't stop you being attracted to other people. There's also a basic human longing for novelty. Sleeping with someone new in your head while in bed is actually a very sensible way to indulge adulterous leanings. Far preferable, I think you'll agree, to doing it in reality. I do need to add a few get-out clauses here though: fantasizing about other people *every* time you have sex with your partner isn't a great sign, and there's evidence that fantasizing about the *same* person – particularly someone who's available in real life – could feed the desire to act on it. Otherwise, it's one of the best ways to keep sex hot long term.

04 You follow the same pattern

Most couples make love in the same way, for the same length of time, nearly every time they have sex. It's not ideal and I'll be suggesting lots of ways to break the habit. But if it means your sex life is bad, we'd all have to put our hands up. Predictability in lovemaking can be a huge plus. Knowing exactly what's about to happen enhances arousal for people who need to feel "safe" in bed or need set, specific stimulation to orgasm.

Amy, 35, with partner six years
"My partner says he never fantasizes about other women when having sex with me. Personally, I think it's rubbish. Everyone does it, don't they? I certainly do! But because he lied I then had to lie when he asked me. I guess he was protecting my feelings but I would have appreciated honesty more."

05 She needs to DIY

The fact that she's rubbing her clitoris during intercourse means you're both sexually educated enough to know almost all women (around 80 per cent in fact) need clitoral stimulation to orgasm. Penetration alone rarely does it. Some men, however, want to do the work, feeling it will make up for their penis not being enough. The problem is that thrusting, and some sexual positions, can make it incredibly difficult for him to maintain the constant rhythm required. That hand gets knocked around and it's a bit like trying to rub your head and pat your tummy at the same time – trying to thrust with his hips and rub with his fingers isn't easy. Her offering to DIY helps. It also makes sense if she needs a specific technique, done in a certain order and way. It's her body on the end of that hand and if it's her hand, she can then get what she needs. The penetrative orgasm rate for women who do it themselves is way higher than for women whose partners do it for them.

06 You don't always feel like it

We know from celebrity confessions that even those who top the "Sexiest man/woman of the year" lists have "ugly" or "fat" days. Some days our self-esteem is low, sometimes it's high. Of course this is going to filter through to your sex life – and it works both ways: our partners aren't going to look hot all the time either! If you *never* feel sexually attractive and it stops you having sex, it's a problem, but if it's the odd two or three days here and there, don't worry.

07 You like different things

If you know this, it also means you've been honest with each other about what you want. It's more of a problem if you have different ideas of a great sex session but haven't told each other. There are lots of suggestions for how to get around this throughout the book including "take-turn" sex where you each get a turn to have sex the way you want. Another good compromise is to divide up the session to cater for both your needs. If he

But it's not like it is on telly!

Sex offers us many things, not just erotic release. It's also about love, fun, and – crucially – connection to your partner. Very few couples *consistently* have bed-shaking, knee-trembling sex sessions long term. To have that sort of sex, you usually need to *make* it happen. Like try something new and naughty to press fresh buttons. Intense, lusty sex is not the norm long term, but the exception. Other times sex will be a bit of fun, an expression of love, a simple release for a physical need. It's OK for it not to fit the standard model of sex we see on TV where it's all urgent and sweaty.

wants fast, hard sex based around intercourse and you want lots of oral, followed by slow lovemaking with you on top, one compromise might be this: the session starts with "her sex", resulting in an orgasm for her through oral, then continues to "his" style for him to orgasm.

08 Sex doesn't last very long

One study showed seven to 13 minutes of intercourse is not just fine but "desirable". Other research says the average guy climaxes in around four minutes. Regardless of how you stack up against the stats, what's most important is that it's lasting long enough to keep *you both* happy. If one minute is enough, there's no problem. Intercourse that lasts too long is an issue for lots of women. As one of my friends so sweetly puts it: "I have sex much more often with my new guy because he comes quickly. If I'm tired, I know it's not going to take that much effort." Not terribly romantic. But true.

09 It takes time to climax

Apart from this taking up time and energy (see above!), it's only an issue if it bothers you. If you're both willing to allow the time, and happy to have orgasm-less sex occasionally (satisfying sex doesn't have to include an orgasm), it's fine. If it's her, invite a vibrator into the bed. If it's him, he can masturbate to finish himself off

You've both got completely different tastes and ideas on what makes a steamy sex session? Take turns and it's not a problem.

What's really going on long term

The top five reasons for skipping sex are (with respondents allowed to choose more than one reason): too tired (53%), not well (49%), not in the mood (40%), too busy with kids or pets (30%), and work (29%).

Fifty-six per cent of men think about sex daily compared to 19% of women.

A "no-sex" marriage isn't officially total abstinence. Sex therapists brand couples as "no-sex" if they're only having sexual encounters less than 10 times per year. Twenty per cent of American marriages are classified as "no-sex". A "low-sex" marriage is classed as having sex less than every other week, so less than 25 times a year. Fifteen per cent of American couples fall into this category.

The longer a couple avoids sexual contact, the harder it is to break the cycle. It's also true that the longer you go without sex, the less you miss it.

How important is sex to your happiness? The generally agreed on adage in sex therapy is that when sex is going well, it adds 15–20% to your happiness with the relationship. If sex is bad or non-existent, relationship dissatisfaction soars to 50–70%.

The longer you are with your partner, the less sex you have because of what's called "habituation": removal of the novelty factor.

The amount of sex you have falls with age and the length of the relationship. Men and women in their mid-20s to mid-30s have sex an average of eight to nine times a month. Two years in, this drops to six times per month. People under 25 have sex around 11 times a month but even they have it less often the longer they've been with their partner.

How often you have sex in the first year you're together dictates how often you will have sex from then on. Surveys show it sets the pattern – if you're having an above average amount of sex, it continues even after two years when there's a natural drop-off point.

Taking turns to initiate sex and talking about sex are the two most important factors for a satisfying sex life in the long term.

One of the biggest predictors of male sexual satisfaction is receiving oral sex regularly.

Couples have sex with each other less often the longer they are married. Married adults under 30 years old say they have sex an average of 109 times a year. The average drops to 70 times per year for 40-somethings and 52 times a year for people in their 50s.

For 75% of people, lack of time is one of the greatest frustrations of their sex life.

It's normal for 5–15% of sexual experiences to be mediocre or unsatisfying.

In Britain, 55% of the population have sex weekly, with 40% satisfied with that amount. In the US, 48% of the 53% that enjoy weekly sex are satisfied. Sixty per cent of Australians do it weekly, with 42% happy. In Germany, 68% of people are having sex weekly but only 38% are happy with the frequency.

The "seven year itch" is a myth. It was the title of a movie starring Marilyn Monroe that had a fictional book in it, by a fictional author, who claimed men have affairs after seven years of marriage. There never has been any evidence to support it.

Fifteen million men in the US have significant erection problems and another 10 million have partial difficulty. One man in three has some difficulty with his erection by age 60. Out of 500 people visiting their GPs in the UK, one in five has a sexual problem. Difficulties with erections and desires are the most common.

One out of five women doesn't enjoy sex and a quarter of all women say they have difficulty reaching orgasm.

Twenty-five per cent of men say they orgasm too fast.

What's Your Sex Style?

Are you an erotophile or erotophobe? A lusty, adventurous "energizer" or a "connector" who's more interested in connecting hearts than parts? We each have a "sex personality" and understanding each of yours is the key to having great sex together!

The first thing I said to my (now ex) boyfriend was, "Can we please have dirty sex and save all the lovey-dovey, soppy stuff for outside the bedroom?" OK, I'm exaggerating a little but it seriously wasn't that far in and we certainly hadn't "done it" yet. He looked at me in astonishment, then smiled and said "*Hell* yes!" And I practically fell to my knees – no, not for that reason – but to thank God for delivering me a good old-fashioned, filthy-thinking, me-Tarzan-you-Jane, talk-dirty-all-you-want bloke. My previous boyfriend was so deeply in touch with his feminine side, I surreptitiously checked his penis for telltale scars to see if he was, in fact, a woman who'd had gender surgery. Yes, that bad. He was more female than any female I know and incapable of having sex without saying "I love you" at least eight times every three minutes. A match made in sexual heaven we weren't, while my new boyfriend and I – both naughty – were sexually seamless. (Clearly not so flawless outside the bedroom, but hey!)

If you're lucky enough to have hooked up with someone who has the same "sex personality" as you, congratulations! Connecting on this base level means you'll probably have a lot less problems than most. But what if that didn't happen and the person you're desperately, deeply in love with is at the other end of the spectrum when it comes to sexual styles? Are you doomed if your "sex personalities" are different?

The answer, of course, is no. In reality, perfect matches are rare because we tend to be attracted to our opposites in an unconscious attempt to balance ourselves. Besides, there really isn't a perfect couple combination (despite my boasting!) because same-same and opposite-opposite styles can all work equally as well together. The trick is understanding each other's natural preferences and predilections, learning from each other

rather than secretly thinking your own personality is the "right" one, and allowing your differences to complement each other. Like most things in sex, it's all about attitude. You can think it's a huge problem if your partner likes being tied up and the only thing you like tied is the bow on a bouquet. Or you can think, "Wow! They're different from me so I can learn from them." You need to applaud each other's strengths and learn to live with the limitations.

So that's what this is all about: defining your natural sex style in an attempt to understand what comes easily for each other and what doesn't. There's also a section on "erotic blueprints" (see page 26) to help you work out how your parents, childhood, and early sexual experiences have shaped you.

Almost all of the sex therapists I really rate have their own versions of sex personalities. I particularly like the "energizer" and "stabilizer" theory put forward by Sandra Scantling, an outstanding US-based therapist. I've used my own versions but they are inspired by her original model. In my experience, apart from "energizers" and "stabilizers", the most common sex personalities are what I call connectors, controllers, and worriers. Work out which style you most identify with (you can be a blend, but most of us have a predominant style), share with each other – then *viva la difference!*

Adam, 38, with third wife
"This is the first time I've clicked sexually with someone I love. My other wives seemed scared of me. I like exploring and while I'm romantic out of bed, not so much in it. My new wife looks innocent but is *wicked* and that keeps me hooked. I guess there's some truth in the 'madonna-whore complex'."

Energizers

Catch you on a good day and you're an exciting, seductive creature who mesmerizes and dazzles your lovers with bucketloads of confidence, extraordinary technique, and unbridled enthusiasm. The downside is you're a little self-absorbed and like to be top of the game in everything you do – and that includes sex. Your partner is lying there in a pool of sweat, announcing they just had the best goddamn orgasm of their life? You'll find it hard to control a self-satisfied smirk. After all, it was *you* who got them there. Competitiveness also makes for unrealistically high expectations, so if something does go wrong – your erection dares not to be rock hard or you're not lubricating enough to flood the Sahara – you over-react, and this can lead to long-term problems.

Is this you?
- Are you pretty much up for anything? Do you like talking dirty, watching porn, trying out sex toys, and having sex outside?
- Do you dislike rules or compromise and feel sex is self-orientated? When you ask "How was it for you?" do you really mean "How was I?"
- Do you see sex as a source of pleasure and fun, and as a great way to connect to your partner?

Good points: You're highly motivated so you happily match with average or low sex drive people. You put the effort in to capture their interest and constantly come up with new things to keep them fascinated.

Not so good: God help an ungrateful lover who is not interested in making sex a priority or is unenthusiastic about it. You don't mind prompting them but enthusiasm and attitude are everything. They also need to be technically adept to satisfy you.

Make sex better: Yes, yes, we all know you're good at the whole sex thing but there's no need to be scathing of partners who aren't as experienced. And no, it's not acceptable to have a bit on the side just because your partner's not putting out as often as you'd like.

Another potential pitfall – "novelty" is your middle name so there's a tendency for you to rely too much on sexual props. Sometimes you need to put down the toys, whips, porn, and playthings and strip sex back to basics. Get naked, get in the missionary position, look deep into your partner's eyes and connect.

Stabilizers

Cautious and co-operative, you'll do anything for a peaceful life. Kind and generous, you initially present as heaven on a stick, especially to someone who's just emerged, bruised and battered, from a relationship with a demanding energizer. But like them, you have your downsides. You thrive on predictability in sex and would rather give than receive pleasure. You don't like talking about sex problems and tend to clam up.

Is this you?
- Do you get more pleasure giving than receiving?
- Do you feel uncomfortable speaking up about what you need your partner to do to satisfy you?
- Do partners often ask if you enjoy having sex with them because they're not sure?

Good points: Your enthusiasm for giving pleasure is phenomenal – you'll happily settle in to perform oral sex for an hour without once complaining of neck pain so bad, you're about to pass out.

Not so good: Your partner's lucky to get a moan or groan when they reciprocate because you have trouble expressing your pleasure. And you actually *like* routine in your sex sessions – not everyone else does.

Make sex better: You're not keen on confrontation so you bury any sexual resentment – often resulting in problems climaxing or getting aroused. Instead of "paying your partner back" in sneaky, passive-aggressive ways, speak up more (see pages 134–142). Shift the pleasure focus to you: think about what you need and tell your partner you need their help to learn to "take" in bed. Concentrate on how things feel and sensations.

Connectors

For you, sex is more about expressing love and feelings than it is physical release. You're less interested in sexual performance and more focused on the emotional benefits of sex: intimacy rather than orgasm is your aim. You're first in line for the "rom-com" and a sucker for grand gestures of love.

Is this you?
- Are you more inclined to cuddle up than initiate sex?
- Does the emotional temperature have to be just right before you can get in the mood for sex?
- Are you more interested in romantic sex than lusty or "dirty" sex?

Good points: You're a forgiving lover and so long as you feel your partner loves you, will tolerate most sex drives. You're realistic about sex so reasonably easy to please in a physical sense.

Not so good: A lusty but disconnected lover who gets too lost in the physical side leaves you cold. For you, the whole point of sex is to feel closer and connected to your partner. If that's missing, you won't enjoy it.

Make sex better: The relationship isn't always going to be perfect, so you could stand to lower your expectations a little. Be more open to spontaneous sex and try shifting your focus from your heart to other parts. Have "dirtier" sex and push your limits. Mix it up a little: romantic, loving sex is great but so is the throw-each-other-around variety. Read some naughty books for ideas and become more selfish about your needs. Most importantly, don't suffocate your partner sexually by insisting they gaze into your eyes when they'd actually rather be feasting them on other, more interesting parts. Most couples have lots of love, it's sex they're lacking. Forcing your partner to be loving during the few times they get to let out their "sexy" side is like telling a chronic dieter they're allowed one day to "go crazy" – then letting them loose in the greengrocer's rather than chocolate shop.

Worriers

Of all the types, you worry the most about sex. It's not to say you don't enjoy it, it's just something that's often fraught with anxiety for you, and in a society saturated by sex, it's embarrassing to admit you're not frothing at the mouth for it like everyone else. You often feel under pressure to perform and feel inadequate – both in how you look and what you're doing in bed. You may even avoid sex completely out of a fear of failure, preferring to satisfy yourself through masturbation.

Is this you?
- Do you have a naturally low libido – or none at all?
- Have you had some distressing sexual encounters in your past and do you think of sex as something to be feared or disliked?
- Is your self-esteem low both in bed and out of it?

Good points: I don't mean to depress you even further but there really aren't any. This is why of all the types, you need to take the fix-its below most seriously.

Not so good: You may try to hide your "secret" by sleeping around to prove to others (including yourself) that you enjoy being sexually active, or to try to obliterate an unhappy sexual past. You may stay in bad relationships and have "victim" sex, from which you get little or no enjoyment. This isn't good – have sex for the wrong reasons with the wrong person, and you feel used, abused, and even more worthless.

Make sex better: Think about past sexual experiences and work out your erotic blueprint (see page 26). Challenge out-dated beliefs and find new, healthier sex role models that help you to replace the views of puritanical parents, for example. If you're single, stop having casual sex and build your sexual confidence. Talk through your experiences with friends or a counsellor, then look for a partner you think you can trust. If you're unsure, introduce them to close friends before getting sexually involved. A healthy, satisfying sex life is possible once you exorcise your demons.

Controllers

You like routine both in and out of the bedroom and the feeling of being in control. Familiarity might breed contempt in others but for you, it's a turn-on. You dislike change and find it quite stressful so the impromptu sexual surprise that would thrill others, instead freaks you out. Predictable sex that follows a tried-and-true set pattern is your idea of sexual nirvana. It requires little effort and is fulfilling enough to keep you sexually satisfied.

Is this you?

- Do you feel threatened or insulted if your partner wants to try something new sexually?
- Can you only orgasm through a particular, often quite specific technique?
- Would you say you like to be in control of your emotions generally?

Good points: Others might look in and find your sex life a little dull but, in fact, you climax easily. Because you stick to the same method, the path to an orgasm is well travelled and if you train your body to orgasm in a certain way, it reads the signposts easily, identifying predictable triggers to tip you over the edge.

Not so good: Your ideal match sexually is someone like you – more interested in good, regular, satisfying sex than trying new things that might possibly backfire. An energizer would alarm you with their need for novelty, a connector would be too intense.

Make sex better: A certain amount of predictability is fine but too much desensitizes. Try to push at least a little out of your comfort zone to build your sexual confidence. If you feel more comfortable approaching sex in a logical fashion, try drawing up a list of new things to try. Predictable doesn't need to be boring: if you plan some new activities to add variety, you'll still feel in control because you know what's coming. Take baby steps and introduce one thing that you feel in control of rather than pushing yourself out of your comfort zone too quickly.

Predictable doesn't need to be boring: if you plan new activities to add variety, you'll still feel in control because you know what's coming.

Your erotic blueprint

The term "erotic blueprint" was coined by psychotherapist Esther Perel who wrote the rather appropriately titled *Mating in Captivity*, a book about sex in marriage. "Tell me how you were loved, and I'll tell you how you make love" is her basic theory – and she's not alone in her thinking. Most notable experts believe how we have sex as an adult is mostly dependent on our experiences as a child and growing up. Our parents' attitude to sex and early sexual experiences form our erotic blueprints and *every single* sexual encounter after that alters them – we're sexually fluid creatures and constantly changing.

And it's not just the obvious stuff – like whether your parents were Buddhist monks or hippies – that has an effect on your sexual outlook. If your parents encouraged you to be adventurous and take chances, you're likely to turn into a daring lover who's willing to give anything a whirl in bed. If either of your parents was aggressive, any intense emotion – like passion – can feel scary, turning you into a timid sexual partner who's turned off rather than on by grand displays of lust. If one of your parents cheated and the other was left broken-hearted, it's *very* common to turn into a heartless seducer who sets out to "get" and then dump partners in a subconscious attempt to avenge the past. Your dad was a bit of a martyr and your mum a taker? Don't be surprised if you prefer giving to taking in bed. The thing is, to be happy sexually, we need to be generous with both love and lust. We also need to be selfish enough to focus on our own pleasure to have our needs met in bed. The foundations for both of these are set in childhood.

It's our erotic blueprint that determines whether we end up an erotophile or an erotophobe. An erotophile is someone who has positive attitudes and feelings about sex, usually because of parents who had healthy sexual attitudes and early sex partners who added to this healthy, exploratory attitude. If this is you, you see sex as a way and means of expressing love and affection, and connecting with your partner. Sex is good! Bloody good in fact! Erotophobes have negative attitudes and emotional reactions to sex, often due to

How were you loved?

Working out *your* erotic blueprint will help you to understand your prime motivations for sex and how it affects you emotionally as well as physically. So it's a really, *really* good idea for you and your partner to work yours out. Think about things like:
• How do you feel about your childhood? Did your parents make you feel loved?
• Were they affectionate, or uncomfortable with touching and cold emotionally?
• Did your parents hit you or – sometimes equally as damaging – make you feel humiliated?
What we learnt as a child shapes what we think of ourselves sexually now: whether we like being male or female, love or hate our bodies, and love or hate sex. We all unconsciously present our erotic blueprints, all wrapped up in a neat little package, to every single sex partner. Meanwhile, they hand over theirs and we're forced to take it, like it or not. Would help to know what's inside, don't you think?

damaging experiences or messages when growing up. Sexual abuse will obviously turn someone into an erotophobe because sex is then associated with trauma and pain, but strict parents or a restrictive religious upbringing can also cause it. For an erotophobe, sex is a chore and usually done for no other reason than to keep their partner happy. There's no enjoyment in the act and it's not ever something they look forward to.

Some people fall squarely and neatly into one of these camps, but you can fall anywhere between these two extremes. Understanding where you and your partner fit in is crucial to making sex the best it can be. Knowing your partner avoids sex because of a bad experience in their teens makes you feel a lot kinder towards them and less rejected when it happens. Appreciating that trying new things makes them feel threatened means you'll approach them in a subtler, slower way. I know this all seems a bit heavy and it's a lot more tempting to skip straight to the fun new technique bits to get things going again. But if you take the time to do this, you may well find it's the most beneficial exercise in the whole book. Yes, really.

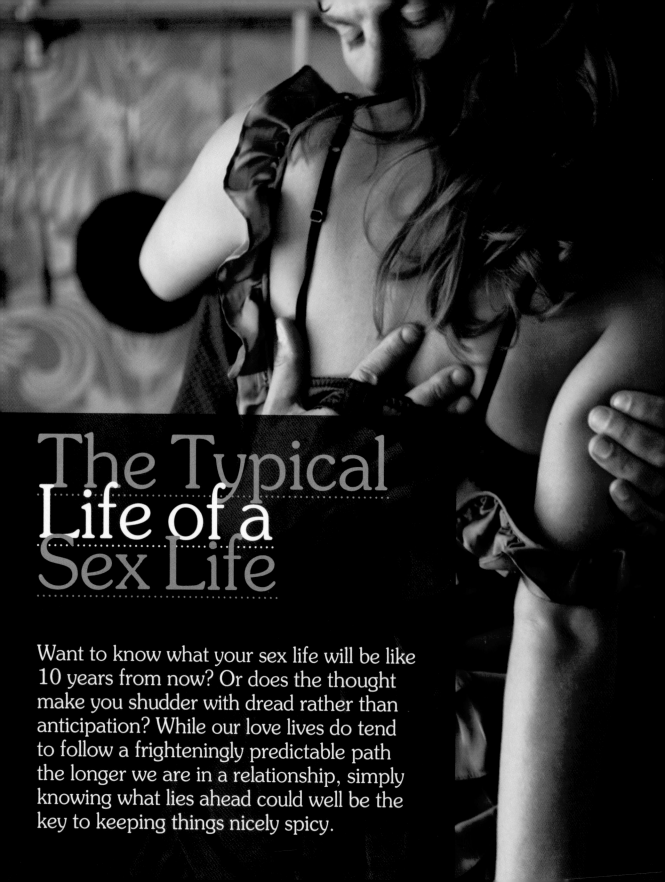

The Typical
Life of a
Sex Life

Want to know what your sex life will be like 10 years from now? Or does the thought make you shudder with dread rather than anticipation? While our love lives do tend to follow a frighteningly predictable path the longer we are in a relationship, simply knowing what lies ahead could well be the key to keeping things nicely spicy.

US psychologist and TV chat show host Keith Ablow says if couples who have been married for 20 years claim their sex life is as good as it was at the start, there are only three possibilities: they're lying, they're telling the truth because they didn't have good sex to begin with, or sex is all they've ever had because they haven't connected emotionally. I have to agree with him. Sorry to be a party pooper, but if you're looking to keep the sex you had in the first few months going forever, you're kidding yourself. It's impossible to achieve. Long-term sex can be bloody good and immensely satisfying – but it sure as hell won't be the sort of sex you had at the start.

An unwillingness to let go of the sex we experience during "limerence" – the first stage of a relationship, when you bonk yourselves silly – is, in fact, a major reason why most of us don't have good sex in the long term. Recognize fresh-flesh-lust for what it is, rather than over-valuing it, romanticizing it, or (the most deluded of all) thinking it's normal, and you've got half a chance of still wanting to get your leg over in your 70s. The trouble is, most of us go into a frothy, manic panic when those first flames die because we think it's possible to make it last, if only we could find the right person. And we still believe this when we're in our 50s, on our sixth marriage, and have 400 notches in the bedpost. Be prepared for what's likely to happen and you're less likely to over-react when things get wobbly, and think things are wrong when they're just part of the cycle of a typical love life.

There are many theories on the stages a relationship typically passes through. Apart from the first stage, dictated by hormones, my experience is couples don't follow set time formulas but move at their own pace,

Michele, 31, married five years
"I haven't had sex with my husband for two years. I have nothing against sex – I actually miss it – but he treats me so badly, I don't think he deserves to enjoy me sexually."

depending on their age, when they got together, their maturity levels, and their relationship history. This is why I've ordered the stages in terms of flow, rather than time spent in each stage. The first three stages are pretty universal to all couples but you might skip some of the other stages, depending on where you are in your relationship life cycle. You'll enjoy reading the first part but brace yourselves: not all that follows is good news. Unless of course you decide to replace unrealistic ideals with sensible ones. That just might get you the fairytale ending you've been searching for.

Limerence and lust

When: Lasts from three months to three years, but most commonly stops after 18 months.

What's happening to your heart and head:
Psychologist Dorothy Tennov first coined the suitably fairytale phrase "limerence" in a book she published in the late 70s. It's now the accepted scientific term for what most of us – rather foolishly and misguidedly – refer to as "love". Limerence isn't in fact love but the act of *falling* in love – a temporary, silly state that can't be sustained both for physiological reasons (the brain hormones that cause it dry up) and practical ones (holding down a job and keeping friendships and small pets alive are impossible while in the grips of it).

"Limerence" is the part when you first meet and become utterly, ridiculously obsessed. You long to be with each other every millisecond of every day and nothing and no-one else matters. If someone called to say you'd won £5 million you'd tell them to get the hell off the phone because your lover might be trying to call. If you're not talking to them, shagging them, or climbing all over them in an attempt to crawl inside, you're daydreaming about doing all three. The two of you blend to become one and see each other as perfect, flawless creatures with zero faults. You are completely immune to logic. Someone points out that a 30-year age difference might be a problem and you smile and say mysteriously, "It might be for other people but not us." The euphoria created by the cocktail of brain hormones released is similar to that created by coke or "uppers". Both raise the level of feel-good chemicals in the brain and high doses of dopamine and serotonin mean you don't need to sleep or eat and have limitless energy.

What's happening in bed: The logic lobotomy instils a smug sense of sexual supremacy. Other couples may suffer the inevitable sex slump that seems to occur after the initial shagfest, but that's not going to happen to you two! You're *different*. There's no way you'll ever get enough of that delicious body and delectable

mouth. You've never had sex like this. Ever. (You have actually, last time round.) It's intolerably exciting, there's lots of it and it lasts for ages. This is called "spontaneous lust", which is entirely effortless. Simply thinking about or seeing your partner is enough to get the juices flowing. Trouble is, the sex isn't real. Quite frankly, you could be shagging a sheep and not realize it because most of the erotic excitement is being produced by the brain hormones rather than what's really in front of you. Low sex drives, appalling technique, a slant towards selfishness – the intense boost you're getting right now cunningly disguises it all. If we could all stay at this point, we would. Sod our job, friends, the poor little children in Bosnia who won't have fresh water without our monthly donation. Nearly everyone gives up and surrenders to the gloriousness.

Keep it going by introducing new sexual adventures – sex outside, a sex toy – *before* the hormones wear off, to artificially extend their lifespan. Step in to create a "chemical kick" early enough and you'll push it past the natural falling point.

Comfort and cuddles

When: Kicks in after limerence ends.

What's happening to your heart and head: The sexy, supercharged brain hormones slow from a flood to a trickle and fuzzy, bonding chemicals like oxytocin and vasopressin move in. The result is a less frenetic, calmer, content phase where affection and love seem more important than getting your leg over in the loo at your friend's dinner party. Depending on your personality, exiting "limerence" leaves you feeling utterly deflated (at which point you physically exit stage left) or slightly relieved. If it's the latter, you quite rightly sense you're about to move into something equally as satisfying, albeit in a different way.

This stage is the precursor to "real" love, sometimes called "loving attachment" or "enduring love". You feel safer and the obsession has a new target – commitment and planning your future. Finally able to relax, he gets to see you without make-up, you get treated to the thrilling sight of him having a poo with the door left open. Both, amazingly, cause "how cute" smiles rather than a dash for the door. Little pot bellies develop but neither of you is concerned because you're convinced you love each other for what's on the "inside". You're in the "nesting" stage and move in together.

What's happening in bed: It's only at this point that you get a true reading of what your sex life is really going to be like. We all have a sex "home base" – a natural libido level created by genetics, hormones, and ageing. It's a set point: the amount of sex we most often want, whether you're in a relationship or not. (If you're solo, you'll masturbate to keep the level constant.) Limerence falsifies our home base because the rush of hormones pushes it much higher than usual. So when the hormones dry up, any mismatch in sex drives starts to become horribly apparent.

People with high sex drives will still want lots of sex because they're naturally predisposed to this frequency. A low sex drive person, robbed of the kick-ass brain cocktail, also reverts to their natural state. Blind lust and raw urgency disappear regardless of your libido because the "newness" has gone and good technique is now necessary to keep you satisfied. This is an *ohmigodpanicpanicpanic* point. Don't. If your sex drives are compatible and you're sexually educated and experienced, you'll cope with the drop in frequency and start talking about what you both like and don't like in bed. Even if the opposite happens, there's *loads* in this book to fix all of these problems. The main thing to realize is this doesn't (necessarily) mean you're with the wrong person. While limerence airbrushes, towards the end of the comfort stage you both pull magnifying glasses out and take a good, long look. This is normal and necessary – love that lasts is based on how you both really are, rather than what you both wanted to see.

Make it better instantly by realizing *everyone* goes through this. Lessen the shock of the bucket-of-cold-water reality check by introducing a strong streak of playfulness into sex. Wrestle around on the bed, laugh during sex when things go wrong. Reassure each other it's normal and even a bit funny to see each other warts and all.

The power struggle

When: Happens either straight after the comfort and cuddles stage or runs in conjunction with it. Lots of couples experience these two stages simultaneously.

What's happening to your heart and head: You're sizing each other up to decide who is going to be "boss" of the relationship. All couples have power struggles – even meek, mild, mousey types – either consciously or unconsciously. And once the swords are drawn, the battle can be bloody and epic. Yikes! You'll both feel confused – what the hell happened to your perfect love affair and sex life?

What's happening in bed: Sex can be used as a weapon – withdrawn as punishment or used to show off your "superior" lovemaking skills. Previously accused of being "lazy" in bed (I'm not talking about myself, obviously, I would *never* be lazy), you're suddenly the one pinning him down on the bed, practically dislocating both your wrist and tongue with dazzlingly impressive manoeuvres to prove who's *really* on top of this whole sex thing. (Again, I'm hardly speaking from experience but has *he* written a dozen sex books? I don't think so!) Now pay attention, boys

and girls, because this is the bit when resentment can crawl under the covers, rudely elbowing out the chocolate body paint. All that arguing is an incredibly effective anti-aphrodisiac – even the healthiest libido flags. The trick to getting through? Think about it. It's fuelled by fear of nearly losing each other, relief at being happy again... that's right, make-up sex!

Embrace the power play instead of fighting it to add risk to your relationship. The first to have the courage to "dirty" the relationship rather than struggle to keep it "pure" is powerful indeed. This means owning up to wanting to do things like tie-up and role-play without worrying you'll lose your partner's love by appearing less than saint-like. You'll also avoid both of you satisfying your dodgier erotic needs with outlets like solo masturbation or internet porn. (They're fine as side dishes but not as main events.)

If the power struggle is so obvious, even the dog's feeling the strain ("Come to Mummy! Good dog! You love Mummy much more than Daddy don't you?"), harness it and turn it into something rather brilliant. Like "competition" sex nights, where you'll come up with marvellously inventive scenarios, desperate to outdo each other.

"Me" as well as we

When: Tends to happen once you've successfully negotiated the power struggle.

What's happening to your heart and head: Having established clear relationship roles, you're both confident enough to separate a little. Realizing it's impossible to be everything to each other, you look outside the relationship to satisfy parts that aren't being fulfilled by your partner. In my case, this usually means admitting I lied about being willing to get up at 4am to watch the Grand Prix. (As if.) And my boyfriend positively refusing to look even remotely interested in discussing the Jungian theory of attraction. (What is wrong with men, really?) If you both hit the separation stage simultaneously, it can be quite liberating. Sadly, this happens about as often as simultaneous orgasms. Usually one is ready to climb out of the couple bubble before the other and one feels hurt and threatened. Realize what's happening and it's easy to negotiate: ladle on the reassurance or ask for it, depending on which side you're on.

What's happening in bed: You start to see differences between you, as well as similarities, in bed as well as out of it. Your idea of a hot session involves filthy porn and nasty-looking sex toys, theirs soft, lingering kisses with "I love you" whispered on every thrust? Great! We're always attracted to what we aren't ourselves. Be open to trying their way and you may find you like it. Even if you don't, you'll establish a nice, healthy sexual give-and-take cycle. There's another bonus: if you're both happy to regain independence, there may actually be a spike in sexual desire. The more you do apart, the more you've got to talk about – and a hint of jealousy and insecurity about what your partner does when you're not around doesn't do either of you any harm.

Reap the benefits of any sudden insecurity by turning the fear of losing your partner into a reason to see them as sexually desirable. Consciously or not, you're secretly cultivating a trustworthy, dependable "comfy slipper" image of them to make yourself feel safe. Deliberately shift it back to seeing them as the sexy, attractive-to-everyone person you were initially drawn to. Your heart will feel nervous but desire will re-emerge along with wanting to please them sexually to keep them. Lust is in the longing and that decreases the more we know we've won the heart of someone. This won't come easy (though you might, if you can manage it!) but it's crucial to keeping you two happy long term. (Much more on this later.)

The chaos of kids

When: The second the first one pops out the womb.

What's happening to your head and heart: Nothing, but nothing, stresses a relationship more than children do. Forget the romanticized view of the two of you gazing down at an angelic, sleeping child. My friend Sarah has twins. She said she's so worn down from the relentlessness of it all, she couldn't even summon up the energy to say "hello" when her husband came home after a four-day conference. "My first thought was 'You bastard. You've had time off.'" You're both struggling to reconcile your new roles of "Mum" and "Dad" with your former sexy selves, and see each other completely differently. Let's face it, picture "parents" and you won't conjure up an image of a couple lustily going at it.

What's happening in bed: Absolutely nothing. And it's not just sleep deprivation that's stopping sex. If he was at the wrong end of the birth, her vagina has transformed from sexual heaven into a holy place that delivered his *child* (it seems wrong to go there for selfish sexual reasons). Or he views it as a messy, bloody, godawful hell hole that wasn't looking it's most attractive and caused such pain it made his testicles shrink to peanuts. Meanwhile, the physical contact she's getting from nurturing a baby nicely replaces what she got from him. Either that or she's so tired of giving so much to the baby, the thought of having to give to him as well is about as welcome as haemorrhoids. Your children suddenly have horns growing out of their heads? Sorry to deliver such slash-your-wrists type news but couples who rather sensibly decide to expect little from their sex and love lives for the first two years survive the best. It's a temporary stage, you're not kissing goodbye to sex forever. (Yes, I know, by God it feels like it, but it really does get better – see opposite).

Skate through it by talking about how much you both miss sex, reassuring each other it will return. Replace spontaneous desire with receptive desire: desire you need to create. This is why even one or two naughty weekends away per year are crucial.

Settling in

When: The kids are growing up or you didn't have any and have been together six years or more.

What's happening to your heart and head: With kids, you're functioning – "functional" also being the description of your relationship. With lives dictated by children, personal needs limp along behind, like a poor cousin dressed in threadbare hand-me-downs. Your partner is useful (for the school run/to drop Cindy off to that party) rather than a source of fun or pleasure. Chores are divided between you with ruthless efficiency. But… there's a deeper intimacy because you're both (rather smugly) aware that you're performing the altruistic task of moulding future generations. And this is when the soppy moments you expected at the start really do happen. You look at each other when the kids do something cute and think, "Wow! We did this together." *Awww.*

If you don't have kids, the relationship moves from "fun" to "functional" because something is invariably introduced to take their place. It's usually joint projects like doing up the house, starting a business, planning exotic travel together, or focusing on "substitute kids" like pets. Child-free, your relationship survives better because you have more time for each other (assuming that not having children was a choice, rather than a complication – if there's resentment over this, please consider seeing a counsellor because the fallout can be devastating). In both cases, your partner morphs from someone erotic to a source of safety.

What's happening in bed: This is another crucial sexual stage because you've been so wrapped up in the kids, you forget about each other. If sex got "parked" when the kids were little and neither of you has enthusiastically suggested reintroducing it, it's because the less sex you have, the less sex you tend to want. This is also when having no sex becomes the "elephant in the room". But don't panic: it can be fixed (see page 76). Or maybe you're having sex but it's, well… *mind-bogglingly boring*? That's probably because it's turned into maintenance sex – done out of physical need and habit rather than with passion or creativity. If one of you is initiating sex

but being rejected, you may feel sexually abandoned and angry. The other may be suffering from some form of sexual dysfunction – erection problems, pain on intercourse, lack of desire – but be too embarrassed to tell. I'm not going to lie to you: this is the hardest stage to survive. The average duration for failed marriages in the Western world is 11.3 years. This is the bit where all the clichés apply – you may feel taken for granted, ignored, or that you've grown apart. This book will help with the sexual side but if things are getting out of control, seek counselling (see pages 183–185).

Stop your sex life sliding down the drain by having a serious sex talk (see pages 134–42). If you can't thrash out deep-seated problems, see a sex therapist (see pages 183–185). Take control rather than letting this stage control you and you *can* make it through. Don't assume you know everything about each other sexually. Many couples are together for a decade and still don't know their partner's secret sex turn-on. Open up about one of your own and they may well follow suit. Think of this as an opportunity to start afresh with sex; you are ending one era and beginning another.

> **Debbie, 39, married 18 years**
> **"People say it's boring not to have variety and that it's the most dreadful thing in the world to sleep with the same person forever, but I see it as a positive. It's reassuring, not boring. I'm also quite insecure about my body so would find it incredibly difficult to expose myself to a new person who might be critical. I can't imagine stripping for a stranger, I'd be terrified! One partner for life is a huge plus of monogamy for me."**

Growing old together

When: Typically in your 50s or early 60s.

What's happening to your heart and head: Your kids leave home, your parents die, one or both of you retires. If your relationship is good, the result is a fizzy, fresh chance to focus anew on each other. There's an acceptance that change is unlikely. This breeds either a contented, "Looks like we're stuck with each other" companionship or complete, abject, throw-yourself-off-a-cliff type despair. Either way, the news can be positive. You're less worried about what people think so finally have the courage to leave and meet someone else. (Fifty-plus is a fast-growing section of the dating market.) If being contented kicks in, you're up for trying things once seen as "inappropriate". Hence grannies taking up sky-diving or wrinklies jetting to Amsterdam to gawp in the windows of the red light district.

What's happening in bed: You might not have sex often but the quality can be very good now that you're giving each other your full attention. Health problems can take their toll but it's possible to beat the ageing blues by playfully pointing out problem areas rather than trying to cover them up. If you can rib each other about parts that don't look so hot, there's less embarrassment.

In love again

When: You've ridden the relationship rollercoaster and now have matching zimmerframes parked at the door.

What's happening in your heart and head: It's an apt reward that couples who manage to negotiate all the hazards of long-term love get to once more experience the heady, intense emotions that started them out on the relationship rollercoaster. This is why older couples often seem the most romantic of all – it's sparks of a renewance of "limerence" that are putting the twinkle in your eyes. Just as you did at the start, you now only have them for each other. Except this time, the rush of all-consuming tenderness and togetherness is created by a lifetime of memories rather than the promise of one.

What's happening in bed: Research suggests plenty of people at 70-plus rate their sex lives as "very satisfying". The orgasm quota isn't what it was, but sex is slow, sensual, and high on snuggling and cuddling.

Potential problems? Grandkids are lovely but don't let them interfere with the utter contentment you get from being in your own bubble. Enjoy every second together and relive your naughty sexual encounters along with the "Wasn't that a marvellous holiday?" moments.

What I've learnt so far...

To accept sex can't be perfect. I won't fall for myths and will set real expectations about what I'd like to achieve and change.

To understand and enjoy the differences between my partner and me rather than try to turn them into "mini-me".

To sort out problems in my sexual past so I can have happy sex in the future.

To accept that most couples fall in and out of love during the course of a relation-ship. It's normal to have highs and lows and nothing to be frightened of.

To not over-react if we go through a low- or no-sex period, but not to ignore it either. Sex "droughts" are normal at some stages but warning signs in others.

To stop comparing my relationship to other couples who are at a totally different stage.

2
The
Erotic
Marriage

You need a strong foundation – to understand each other as much as possible – for the yummy, fun, hands-on stuff to work.

Just Who Are You Sleeping With?

You may think you know your partner…
but do you? Take a step back from focusing
purely on the two of you and, instead, look
at your relationship *style* for some fresh,
surprising insights set to perk up both your
sex life and relationship!

We all like to think we're highly individual, skipping about the planet as
unique as fingerprints, but the truth is, emotionally and sexually, we're
all more alike than we are different. Pretty much all of us, for instance,
fall into a surprisingly small number of relationship styles. And it's these
that dictate how we love and have sex… or don't. It seems the key to still
wanting to throw a leg over your partner 30 years in, is as much about
understanding your relationship *style* as it is about your – and your
partner's – deep, dark urges and yearnings.

As always, theories abound on the range of categories, each researcher
or therapist putting their own particular spin, stamp, or signature flourish
on the generally agreed-on basics. Not to be outdone, I've done the same
here. (Though if you'd like to explore alternatives or the topic more
thoroughly, my pick of the pack would be author and sex therapist Jack
Morin or Kathleen Cervenka, a US psychotherapist.)

Now, if you've been reading this book in order, you should be a few steps
in to building up a clear picture of what's *really* happening in your relationship. The first part identified what's normal and what's not in whatever
stage of love you're in and talked about your individual sexual influences.
This chapter focuses on sex and relationship issues that affect the *two* of
you. The following "analyse-this" features are designed to round off the
process. Stick with it. You need a strong foundation – to understand each
other as much as possible – for the yummy, fun, hands-on stuff to work.

Every couple is a blend of all "marriage" styles to a certain extent but usually have a predominant category they most identify with. Is there a "perfect" style that guarantees lifelong lust and love? "Passionate" couples are probably the closest to the ideal – which could explain why they're the least common. Second on the wish list is the "healthy" couple. These tend to be quite long-term couples who've openly confronted the difficulty of maintaining both passion and closeness – so are the ones most likely to get it.

Interestingly, it's the couples who describe each other as "best friends" who struggle the most sexually. A great relationship ironically often means a mediocre sex life – it's the turbulent, on-again, off-again, who-the-hell-would-want-it sort of liaisons, constantly ripped apart by fights that would send most of us scuttling to the divorce lawyer, that enjoy the highest erotic spark. In other words, whatever your style, there are pluses and minuses. Some make for a better sex life, some a better love life. Recognize yours, work on the weak parts and nurture the strengths, and *you* might just be the lucky bastards who end up with both!

The disconnected couple

Love: It's easy to spot someone who is disconnected from their partner. It's the guy striding three paces ahead of his wife. The girl you've worked with for three years and never knew she was married because she talked in "I"s not "We"s. They're one foot in, one foot out people. Disconnected people don't just guard their individuality by standing separate from their partner, they put ex-MI5 agents with bazookas on the border.

Why are they so protective of themselves? They're terrified they'll lose themselves in a relationship. Is your partner more concerned with their own needs than the needs of the relationship? If yes, tick this box. Self-absorbed, disconnected people tend to see friends solo and often plan weekends away without their partner. Physical distance usually translates to emotional distance so while they're affectionate, it's friendly and controlled rather than the tender, look-deep-into-my-eyes variety.

Having sex with someone who's disconnected is a bit like making love to a shadow or a ghost. "It's like 'Hey, I'm here but where are you?'"

Sex: Having sex with someone who's disconnected is a bit like making love to a shadow or ghost. "It's like 'Hey, I'm here but where are you?'" says the ex of a deeply disconnected man. Some will invent excuses to sleep in separate bedrooms in a bid to get space. Having said that, others are so good at putting up boundaries, they make quite lusty lovers. They have no problems separating sex from love and so long as it's lust you're after and not intimacy, it can work.

Sex it up

- **It is possible to love and not sacrifice yourself.** Try letting your partner in, a little at a time, and you'll discover that not all intimacy is stifling.

- **Stop fighting so hard for your independence and, instead, try to connect.** A relationship isn't a jail but a place you've *chosen* to be. Not all requests for affection or connection are dastardly bids to secretly take away your freedom.

- **Shift your focus from you to them.** Pay more attention to your partner's needs in bed and less attention to your own. Stay in the room rather than drift off into fantasy. Make eye contact during sex. Talk to them.

- **Think "I want to" not "I have to".** True commitment-phobes see obligation everywhere. The simplest request becomes an outrageous demand. Consciously shift your mindset. Think "I want to do this" rather than "They're making me do this".

The over-involved couple

Love: At the opposite end of the scale, you have Tweedledum and Tweedledee: the over-involved couple. This pair don't just merge, it's impossible to tell where one ends and the other starts. Ask her something and he'll answer: they're the couple at the end of *When Harry Met Sally*. Single people often walk away from an over-involved couple with a sigh, dreaming of such closeness. Problem is, it's all a little

too close. They don't have a clear sense of their own identity, so instead they become whoever their partner seems to want. It's the "I am who I go out with" syndrome – your strictly vegan girlfriend who's suddenly tucking into a steak because her new lover likes meat. Unlike a disconnector, the over-involved couple have virtually no boundaries. They don't share a life with their partner, they live their life *for* them.

Sex: Sex feels a little incestuous because the over-involved couple act more like siblings. Because their main purpose in life is to please each other, there's zero tension in the relationship. Great for a peaceful life, but sex is drearily dull when neither of you is game to suggest anything for fear the other might not like it. The only argument they're ever likely to have is fighting over who's going to be the one to "give" in bed.

Sex it up

- **Don't confuse your needs and feelings with your partner's.** You are two separate people and the more separate you are, the more you'll appreciate each other. Spend more time apart even if it's in small ways, like popping down the shop solo. Don't let your partner "choose" everything for you – from what TV show to watch to what you'll do in bed that night. Even if you agree, force yourself to suggest something else. Create a difference if there isn't one.

- **Give sex the importance it deserves.** Of all the relationship styles, yours is the first sex life to fall on the sword. Even worse, neither of you particularly cares because it's comfort not desire that motivates you. Affectionate sex is fine but it's not terribly motivational. There's a danger one or both of you will lose interest altogether. Of all the couples, you're the ones who most need to schedule in regular sex time.

- **Masturbate solo and read or watch erotica.** A good-quality vibrator used often will keep her sex drive nicely purring along. It takes bugger-all time to orgasm and is zero effort. Meanwhile, he can explore erotica to get more in touch with sexy scenarios that appeal to *him*, rather than going with the flow. Think about these when you're making love to keep you focused on the sexiness of the session, not the emotional connection.

The companionate couple

Love: Similar to over-involved couples, but much healthier, are what sex therapist Jack Morin calls "companionate couples". These are the "I knew at once that I'd met my soulmate" couples. They're so compatible, it's like they were somehow *meant* to be together. They do most things together but aren't joined at the hip like the less healthy over-involved couple. Totally comfortable with each other, this pair also trust each other implicitly.

Sex: The high friendship factor means sex isn't exactly red hot but if lusty sex isn't a huge priority, this type of pairing can be incredibly satisfying.

Sex it up

- **Don't let love eclipse sex.** Your danger zone is you'll start to see each other as friends not lovers. Try something radical that will force your partner to see you differently. Offer to give oral sex but refuse to finish unless they pay you. Confess a fantasy of stripping in a bar. Anything that shocks them into seeing you as a purely sexual object.

- **Make time for sex.** Of all the clichés, this is one you need to pay attention to. You make time for work, for your family, for your kids. Make time for sex or risk losing your relationship. Don't kid yourself spending time together is a substitute for having sex. It's not.

- **Don't let sex droughts last too long.** "I haven't seen a couple who were able to rebuild a sexual connection after they stopped thinking of each other in an erotic way for five or more years," says Morin. Do it now and do it often.

Confess a fantasy of stripping in a bar. Mock fight. Do anything that shocks them into seeing you as a purely sexual object.

The practical couple

Love: As the name suggests, these two are together for practical reasons. She was looking for a man who'd be a great dad. He wanted someone who'd make him look good at corporate dinners. Whether it's money, looks, status, availability, or convenience, the motive to merge came from the head not the heart. But don't be too hasty to dismiss this logical lot as misguided, cold, calculating creatures. Their relationships often last longer than the others! Because they didn't start out with romanticized views of grand passion or undying love, their expectations are far more realistic. And studies continually show a huge factor in staying together long term is commitment to the commitment. Just as some arranged marriages thrive because the people in them grow to respect and love the person that's been chosen for them, the same can happen here for the practical couple.

Sex: Sexual passion might be lacking at the start but if there's a genuine desire to please – in order to keep what you chose – it can work.

Sex it up

• **Focus more on emotion and feeling.** Because you're usually left-brain driven (the logical side of your brain), there's a tendency to ignore the emotional side. Pay attention to it. Don't dismiss emotions or feelings you have as "silly".

• **Develop sexual confidence.** Practical people often don't like losing control so find it hard to immerse themselves in sex. Try to let go more. If you don't think you're very good in bed, read some sex books. Ask lots of questions of each other to get feedback. The more confidence you have about your sexual skills, the more inclined you'll be to speak up if your needs aren't getting met.

• **See your partner as an individual.** Most of us have a set idea of what people like in bed: women like their breasts fondled, men like blow jobs, you should have sex twice a week. If someone doesn't conform to our personal norm, we tend to think something's wrong with them. Move away from this. Expect differences

John, 42, with partner eight years

"I think you both have an obligation to have sex even when you don't feel like it. I have quite a high sex drive but there are times when I don't fancy it but I still oblige if Karen initiates. It's not only polite, I rarely regret doing it afterwards. Even if the sex isn't that great, I feel like I've given her pleasure and we feel bonded again. Nothing feels better than cuddling after you've just had sex. It's about intimacy as much as physical pleasure."

and you'll work out a compromise. Show surprise, disappointment, or get upset and you can ruin your sex life before it's even begun.

The passionate couple

Love: These are the classic, deeply in love couples you see depicted in films. They're usually opposites who've attracted but, rather than feeling threatened or unsettled by their differences, love the intensity this creates. This pair fall in love quickly and hard. There's so much passion, it obliterates practical considerations like basic compatibility – well, it does at the start. Most passionate love affairs crash and burn as quickly as they began. But the lucky few who negotiate the many hurdles, end up with the relationship the rest of us desperately want: one that's overflowing with buckets of attraction and chemistry.

Sex: There's lots of it and it's usually fantastic. The less "samey" the couple, the higher the sexual heat.

It's those turbulent, who-the-hell-would-want-it sort of liaisons, constantly ripped apart by fights that would send most of us scuttling to the divorce lawyer, that enjoy the highest erotic spark.

Sex it up further

- **Don't get smug because you're the couple we all envy.** Yes, we know sex between you is spectacular but that doesn't mean you don't have to do anything other than congratulate each other. You need to make less effort than others, but you do still need to make an effort.

- **Don't think you know all there is to know about each other.** Lashings of lust smoothes over any technical flaws but it won't forever. Don't just rely on non-verbal cues but talk about your needs because they change constantly and you may have misunderstood them at the very start. It's easy to do. She pushes your hand away from her breast and you think she doesn't like them fondled. Instead, she was just at a tender time in her cycle. Talking about sex isn't just done for communication but to boost sexual confidence as well. Keep laying on the compliments, even if you feel it's obvious you're enjoying it.

The healthy couple

Love: Healthy couples, as you may have guessed, are less common than you think. It requires a delicate balancing act of each of you retaining your own individual identity and personality but also drawing a clear line around the relationship itself, so you're connected to each other. Put simply, you care about both yourselves and each other, in a healthy proportion. At a party the healthy couple won't spend the whole night standing next to each other but they will constantly maintain a connection. It could be by delivering a drink unasked if they see their partner's glass is empty or depositing a kiss on their way to chat to someone. Even if you don't know the couple, you'll know they're together.

Open about everything, the healthy couple discuss the lot, but while they argue, it's infrequent and rarely nasty. This is because even big problems are always approached with a "we'll get through this together" spirit and while they're not frightened to confront reality, there's a constant focus on the positive. No threats, just solutions.

Sex: Because both of you look after your own sexual needs as well as each other's, sex is usually pretty satisfying. Not as scorching as the passionate pair but still pretty damn good!

Sex it up

- **Beware the gruesome twosome.** Boredom and a lack of enthusiasm are things even happy couples battle. The closer you get, the less you feel like sex and the more you settle into routine sex. Expect for this to happen – then fight it. Suggest and be open to constantly trying new things. Encourage each other to see yourselves as sexual partners as well as best mates.

- **Get outside.** The more you're both out there in the big wide world – either together or solo – the more the attraction for each other grows. Why? Well, because as much as it's tempting to stay cuddled on the couch once you've found "The One", you end up taking each other for granted. Seeing someone surreptitiously eye up your partner might hurt your heart but it works wonders for your sex life. Morin calls it "the re-emergence of the self": you see your partner as separate from you rather than attached. A little insecurity actually heightens your interest in each other.

- **Masturbate solo.** This is what will stop you straying (and, kid yourself all you like, being in love does not mean you won't want to rip someone else's knickers off… badly). Many people who are still in lust long term, report having an active private fantasy life where they masturbate to images of other people they're attracted to. In almost all cases, it benefits the relationship you're in rather than threatens it. Just do both of you a favour and don't confess who you're doing it with in your head. Is there anything to be gained from admitting you've had 3,000 solo sex sessions with the should-be-locked-in-an-attic-they're-too-young-to-be-so-hot shop assistant at Starbucks, running scenarios in your head that would make Samantha from *Sex and the City* blush? I think not. Masturbating is also the best way to cope with desire difference. Fancy a bit but they're not keen? Indulge in another mental sex fest rather than hassle your partner.

Toxic Lust
Killers

You can't have great sex if your relationship is in tatters. Identify the deadly sex poisons that could be threatening yours and get set to confront them head on!

This is a "wake up and smell the coffee" story. This book can and will make your sex life the best it's ever been, but in order to do it, you have to be realistic about any issues that may be getting in the way. This means taking a brutally honest (perhaps depressing) look at the state of your relationship. Toxic lust killers are things that poison your sex life. We all battle with some of them – even happy couples! – and you have two choices of how to deal with them. You can stick your heads in the sand like ostriches and pretend nothing's wrong and they may go away for a little while. But long term, this will achieve absolutely nothing. The longer a problem continues, the harder it is to solve. The second choice is to confront them head on. Be brave! Read this, be honest with yourselves about things you're struggling with, then sit down and have a bloody good long talk about where

you're at. Get help if you need it. Good psychologists aren't magicians but they can sure as hell work some magic if you commit to change. It's pointless reading the rest of the book unless your foundations are solid. Dazzling new techniques, *Kama Sutra*-style sex positions, supermodel sex sandwiches – none of these are going to do diddly squat if you can't actually bear the sight of each other.

The following pages are designed to help you identify your demons and confront them. You can't change the past but you can stop these demons controlling and destroying your future. We're all guilty of making mistakes. We've all done things that we aren't proud of. Put your hands up and take responsibility for your part, get help if you need it, but then let it go and allow yourself to move forward.

Commitment
and getting married

"Not tonight dear, we're married" isn't just a cutesy, funny little line they throw around in sit-coms, it's reality for a lot of couples. Twenty-eight per cent of women in one extensive sex study said their husbands stopped wanting sex with them mere months after they got married. "I felt like when I flung the bouquet at the wedding, I was actually throwing away my sex life!" said one newly-wed. And don't feel too smug if you're live-in lovers: non-married couples, together more than two years, report a higher rate of "no" or "low sex" in their relationship than married couples!

A common perception is that it's the wives who start saying "no", having "bagged their man". But it's actually more often *men* saying "I don't" after "I do". Familiarity is a desire dampener for both sexes because it instantly strips away the three top turn-ons: unavailability, adventure, and mystery. For men, commitment also feeds into their age-old primitive belief that once the chase is over and the prey conquered, it's no longer worth having.

"Great!", I hear you mumble, "if your husband or wife isn't a 'sure thing', what's the point?" After all, this sexual security is what fills our grateful hearts with comfort. Down below, though, there are grumbles – "I've already done her or him, I want someone new to play with!" – and foot stamping. The things that drive pre-commitment sex – novelty, risk-taking, going all out to make the person fall in love with you, pushing boundaries – all disappear with commitment.

Then there's the sharing-the-bathroom bit. No one is perfect and this becomes horrifyingly apparent once you're living with someone. Like, "*Ewwwww!* Do you have to cut your toenails at the breakfast table?" No longer idealized, sex drops in priority to something you do after watching TV and before going to sleep. A natural reaction is to feel cheated and deflated, but this isn't going to get you anywhere. What will, is to stop making pre-marriage comparisons and replace the hot, urgent sex of old with something equally satisfying: sex where you know each other's triggers so well, orgasms are guaranteed. Anticipatory sex, where you're both in a hot fluster all day at work because you're about to try something new and naughty that night, is also a more than adequate stand-in.

Anger and resentment

Chronic anger will poison your relationship and sex life. If the person you're living with is no longer your friend, they're the enemy. Why would you want to open your heart – or legs – to them? They can't be trusted to do the right thing by you. Feeling attacked isn't sexy. Attacking someone you're meant to love isn't sexy either. Simmering below chronic anger is resentment: get told off often enough and you feel nagged. Hate starts elbowing love in the ribs. If you're the one doing the telling off, you're fuelled by frustration and disappointment. Self-esteem, for both of you, plummets faster than an out of control lift.

This, my friends, is what's not so affectionately known as marital hell. Interestingly, it's likely to be problems outside the bedroom – not sex problems – that got you here. Think back to when it all started and you'll find the cause; all the other grievances are lumped on top. If you feel angry with your partner or they are angry with you, see a good couples counsellor now. Like, *right now*. Great sex can cure a lot of things, but it's impossible to *have* great sex if anger and resentment are standing by the door watching you and sneering.

Kate, 26, with partner eight months

"My ex-husband constantly put me down and made me feel small and insignificant. I hated sex with him and it took me a long time to regain my confidence. But now I'm with someone who makes me feel good and my libido has returned. For me, how your partner treats you out of bed is more important than what they do in it."

01

Get your pleasure elsewhere. *Food is a source of pleasure but it's not the only pleasurable thing to do. Think about what you could do instead.*

02

Get help if you need it. *But choose a weight-loss system that focuses on feelings about food as well as a plan for healthy eating.*

03

Help your partner *by encouraging them to go on a "health kick" with you. Hopefully they'll take the ball and run with it – literally.*

04

Reward every pound lost *with compliments galore. How much sexier they look, how proud you are... you get the idea.*

Bored or taking each other for granted

"You're either single and lonely or married and bored," says the comedian Chris Rock. There's a strong element of truth in that statement. We spend our lives desperately searching for someone to share them with. Then when we get them, we're bored having to hang around the same person all the time. Boredom and taking each other for granted tend to go hand-in-hand. Stop noticing all your partner does for you and expect they'll always be there, regardless of how you treat them, and you can also kiss goodbye to your sex life.

who cheated, guilt sits on your shoulder during sex, creating an unhappy threesome. You feel bad, shameful, hate yourself for "letting the side down". Or you have regrets about ending it: sex with your lover was hotter because forbidden sex usually is. (Turn to page 124 if you're struggling with this one.)

Sex replacements

Men particularly are guilty of this – if sex with their wives takes too much effort, they'll sometimes take the easier option and replace it with masturbating to net porn, visiting strip clubs, and getting lap dances.

Stop making pre-marriage comparisons and replace the hot, urgent sex you used to have with something equally as satisfying.

Bad or boring technique

The better sex is, the more you'll want it. It really is that simple. While sexual technique can easily be learnt with self-education and feedback from a partner, if you didn't speak up at the start, it seems both cruel and unthinkable to turn around now, 15 years into the relationship, and say "Honey, everything you do in bed doesn't do a thing for me". (It *can* be done nicely – turn to page 134 if this is you.)

Mismatched sex drives

This is a huge problem for lots of couples. Constantly feeling pressured to have sex or having your advances rejected, depending on what side you're on, nearly always results in a bed stalemate. Add lots of simmering resentment to this and the atmosphere becomes deeply *unsexy*. Don't panic – there's loads on overcoming this in chapter three.

Feeling misunderstood and not heard

Otherwise known as the "Why should I have sex with you? What have you done for me lately?" feeling. Females typically complain their partners don't understand them. In the early days of your relationship he'd at least make an attempt to listen to you articulate your emotions but now he doesn't even pretend to make the effort. On his side, he's feeling confused. Because they're left-brain driven, men often aren't very good at the whole "let's talk about emotions" stuff. What comes easily to us women, is hard work for them. You wanting to analyse your feelings is the equivalent of him asking you to take the lawnmower apart to find out why it's not working – and then put it back together again. See pages 134–142 for how to communicate with each other more effectively.

Inhibitions and negative attitudes

Sex is fun. Well it is for people who have a positive attitude to it. If you see it as "dirty" or even scary, it's not much fun at all. A terrifying estimate is that 90 per cent of us have had negative sexual experiences. Not just serious ones – like abuse or rape – but being made to feel not good enough, rejected, or made fun of. (For more on this, see page 26).

An unhealthy lifestyle

A little bit of what you fancy may well release inhibitions and lead to a damn good rogering. But excessive and prolonged use of alcohol and party drugs depresses the central nervous system, numbing sensation and your sex drive. Cut back, or get help if you can't do it alone. Poor health generally is a libido dampener. Who the hell wants sex if they're not feeling well? You know what to do: exercise, eat healthily, get enough sleep...

Getting old

Hit 40 or 50 and your bum isn't the only thing starting to sag. Getting an erection isn't as easy as it used to be – a glimpse of a breast isn't enough and hands-on stimulation is needed. Some men accept this, albeit begrudgingly, but others panic and avoid sex to avoid feeling like a failure. Women tend to hit their sexual peak in their 30s: the path to orgasm is well travelled, they lubricate easily, and are sexually savvy enough to know what they need and demand what they want. In your 40s and 50s, the process of menopause begins and sex can be a dry, painful, joyless affair. It's easily fixed by adding lubricant or going on HRT but again, attitude is everything. We all get old. No one likes it but what's the alternative? Sit in the freezer for the next 20 years and hope like hell you stay preserved?

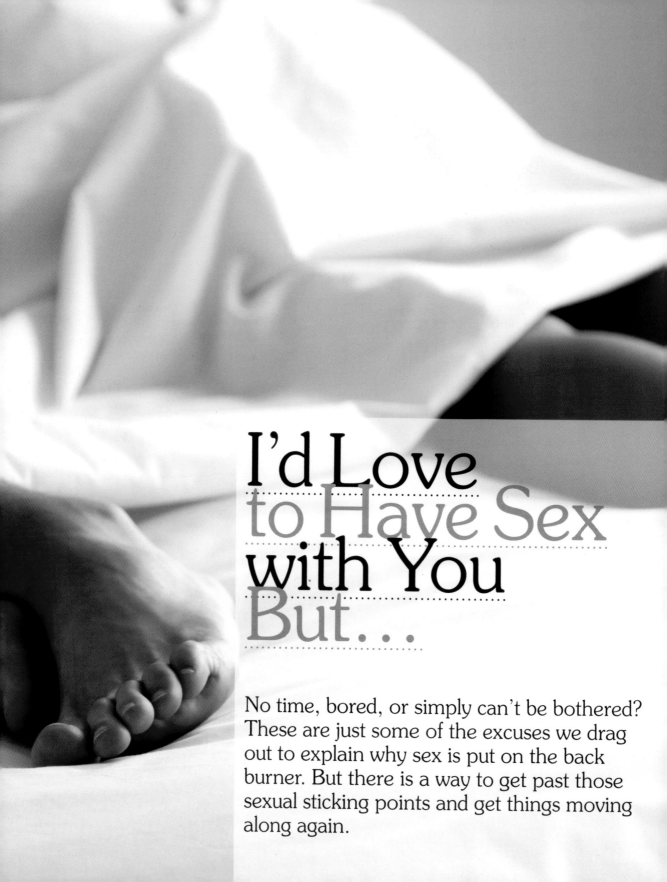

I'd Love
to Have Sex
with You
But...

No time, bored, or simply can't be bothered? These are just some of the excuses we drag out to explain why sex is put on the back burner. But there is a way to get past those sexual sticking points and get things moving along again.

There's no time

Seventy-five per cent of couples say lack of time is the biggest frustration in their sex life. Is this true? Or are we using it as a cop-out? Mira Kirshenbaum, author of *The Weekend Marriage*, actually took the time to calculate how much time we really do have left over in a week, taking into account work, doing chores, looking after kids, spending time on our appearance, watching TV, social obligations, cooking, eating, and sleeping. Her conclusion: out of the 168 hours per week allotted to us, there's only between half and one hour per day left to devote to our partner. So we're not telling fibs: we really are busy… Or are we? Her estimate included 20 hours of TV watching per week. Cut that back (yes you can) and it's looking much healthier.

So there is time for sex – but given time for each other is limited, I'd heartily recommend you *don't* shag all of it away. Sex and love are interdependent and you need to satisfy both sides to make either work properly. So while sex should definitely get a look-in, you also need to use that free time to do whatever makes you feel close to your partner. And don't expect to agree on what that is or be able to second-guess what it is for each other. We all have a nasty habit of clinging on to something that worked in the past, thinking it's going to work now. "He adores it when I cook him a nice dinner," might have been true when you were kid-less. Now, he'd probably prefer to have a takeaway and get more of your attention. She may have waxed lyrical when you first bought her chocolates. Now she looks ruefully at her waistline and wishes you hadn't. Rethink what does it for each of you and then be fair with the time-sharing.

As for sex, get into the habit of having quick sex sessions and deliberately turn yourselves on by re-running previous hot sessions in your heads. Send each other "slutty" texts, suggestive emails, read an erotic book in the loo, have a sneak peek at online porn. All will ensure you're ready to pounce in the short amount of time you do have free. Apply the same efficiency you do to the rest of your life: what gets you both hot and bothered *fast*?

I don't orgasm so why bother?

I'm going to take a stab in the dark here and assume you're female, right? (That's not to say this doesn't happen to men – see page 90 – but it happens much less frequently.) A recent survey found that 56 per cent of women have an orgasm every time they masturbate compared to only 24 per cent of the time when having sex with a partner. So it's a common complaint. But it's still no reason to avoid sex – and it's more easily fixed than you think.

The main reason why most women don't orgasm with their partner is because they don't speak up about what they need to make it happen. If you need 20 minutes of uninterrupted oral sex, ask for it. If fingers on your clitoris during penetration don't work, pull out your vibrator and try that way instead. Ditch traditional thrusting for the more clitoris-friendly grinding or even rocking side to side. How do you have orgasms solo? That's your clue for having them with your partner.

It's not your partner's responsibility to give you orgasms, it's your responsibility to do whatever it takes to get you there. The more passive you are in bed, the less likely it is to happen. Turn things around: be the one who's deciding who does what, where, and when. If you're having trouble getting aroused in the first place, tap into what US sex therapist Jack Morin calls your "erotic memorability". Think back to the sex experiences you've enjoyed the most. What made them stand out? Was it a "first" or something that surprised you? Identify the key elements and work to recreate them. (Within reason, obviously. Doing the hot Italian model you bedded in Ibiza one more time isn't what I had in mind.)

Send each other "slutty" texts, read an erotic book in the loo. All so you're ready to pounce in the short time you do have free.

I never get the chance to initiate

If you're constantly hassled for sex, you don't get the chance to miss it. It's called "the seesaw phenomenon": the more one person does, the less the other does. The more often they initiate sex, the less often you will. Never getting the chance to say "How about it?" is both tedious and demeaning. If your libido's lower than theirs, you already feel you're letting the side down.

Here's how you fix this: tell your partner you miss initiating sex. This alone – I guarantee – will have an extraordinary effect. Especially if you're female. "She's never the one doing the asking" is one of his biggest complaints. He thinks you don't initiate sex because you don't enjoy doing it with him. Simply saying you'd like to be given the chance will score *enormous* points. As much as you're sick of being asked, he's sick of asking. Having to be the initiator is a burden he's carried since school when he tried to persuade Susie to let him go to first base behind the bike sheds. And it doesn't let up. Men are usually more active in bed than women, partly because of their early training to take control, partly because women are shyer about sex, and partly because women need more to arouse them.

Make a pact that he stops making sexual overtures for two weeks. Then around day nine or 10 pounce! Even if your first approach is a bit forced – you're not exactly frothing at the mouth but it might be OK – pretend. Pack the kids off to your mum's and then grab him, push him against the wall, and snog his pants off. His response? "She really wants me. My God, she likes having sex with me after all." Nothing, but nothing, will make more difference to your sex life than you initiating sex more often. (Unless of course he's the one avoiding it, in which case see pages 90-96.) Also think about how you're initiating. Be obvious, direct, assertive. Rolling over and kissing once you're in bed is OK but not terribly original. Think "If I don't have sex with him now I'll die". Studies show that "pretending" passion creates it. Power is a massive turn-on and if you're the one who's up for it and making all the moves, you'll be surprised how turned on you'll feel.

I simply can't be bothered

Oh really? Let me ask you a simple question: do you expect your partner to be faithful to you? If you do, then there's one very good reason for shaking off that apathy. It's called honouring your side of the bargain. If you're in a monogamous relationship, it's reasonable for your partner to expect sex from you on a reasonably regular basis. If you don't intend sticking to your side of the bargain, don't be surprised if they don't stick to theirs and get their needs met elsewhere. If this doesn't bother you, fine. If it does, then something needs to change.

There's always been a good argument for having sex even if you don't feel like it. Sex does one hell of a lot more than simply provide physical release and pleasure. It keeps us connected to our partner, reduces depression, calms us, boosts our immune system, and even helps us to stay young. (It lowers cortisol levels in the blood, which reduces stress and slows the ageing process.) Every time you have decent sex with your partner, your brain sets you up for more good times because it associates them with fun, intimacy – and orgasms. The less sex you have, the less you miss it.

To get yourself out of the rut, consider scheduling sex sessions. It doesn't work for all couples but it works for more than you think. The reason why it works here is that it gives the sex-starved person (that'd be your partner) something to look forward to and the lower sex drive person (hey lazy bones, that's you) time to get themselves aroused. Use the advance warning to build anticipation. Think about what you could do to make this time different, more interesting than the last. Ask your partner to plan some "surprises". Try it. You're reading this book which means you want to want.

Think of it like going to the gym. You have to force yourself the first couple of times but then you start to see results and start to actually enjoy it. Same with your sex life. No pain, no gain. The saying "everything worth having requires effort" is true.

I'm bored of doing the same thing

Humans are creatures of habit and like doing the same things in order. Sometimes this works for us: having a pre-bed ritual, for instance, sends triggers to our brain that we're ready to sleep (there's the make-up remover, it must be time for bye-byes). Watching a loved film a second or third time can be just as enjoyable as the first, but if you watched it 100 times a year – a rough average of how often you have sex – I doubt you'd be quite so enthusiastic. Yet this is exactly what we do in bed: deal up the same old stuff, every single time.

Knowing what's coming next with sex works for some people but not for the majority. It's bad enough only being allowed to make love to the same person, but to do the same thing over and over is sexual suicide. Why do we do it? Well, because it worked in the beginning. They liked it, you liked it. Then there's the fear attached to trying new things. What if they don't like it? Will we look silly or fat in that new position?

Get past this by *both* coming up with something new to try once a week for a month. Do the opposite to what you always do – like try "nasty" instead of romantic sex. Move sex out of the bedroom. Leave on sexy underwear or your high heels rather than strip naked. Rent a hotel room and pretend you're having an affair. Try out sex toys, porn, or a tie-up game. And if all this is sounding wonderfully inventive, for God's sake buy more sex books! Those are just the *obvious* places to start.

Look at the *proportion* of time you spend on what in your sex sessions and mix it up. Two years ago, you told him you want more foreplay, so the poor bugger's still putting in 40-minute oral sessions. There is such a thing as too much foreplay. We all love a massage but if the masseur focuses on the same spot for too long, it changes from heaven to annoying. You start to desensitize and get frustrated ("You've done that bit now, move on! There's only 10 minutes left!") Sex is the same. What feels exquisite to start with can be painful or make us feel numb if it's done for too long.

If they've ignored your request, check it's not a little too out there. A foursome with the two hunky builders renovating the kitchen is a delicious thought, but a tad unfair.

My partner doesn't listen to what I want

When I was younger, I used to HATE my breasts being touched. (Why my nipples suddenly did an about face around 30 is beyond me, but hey, it happened!) When my partner's hands headed that way, I'd say, "I don't like that. Don't know why, but I just don't." I told him at the start, six months in, a year in, and after four years, I left. Not purely for that but it was an indicator of why the relationship failed: he was too self-absorbed to pay attention to anyone's needs but his own.

Given that the majority of people aren't comfortable directing their partner in bed, it's deeply hurtful if you've plucked up the courage to be open about what you want more or less of, only to be ignored. I remember every single thing every single lover has ever told me about what they like or don't like in bed because I think it's incredibly important to make sex pleasurable for your partner. If your requests aren't taken on board, it's insulting. But before you go shouting at them, let's first make sure you've been as clear as you think you've been. Pushing their hand away on the odd occasion could easily go unnoticed. So could pulling them closer when they're doing something right. Subtle signalling doesn't work on all. So if you actually haven't voiced what you do or don't want, do it next time. Say "Honey, that feels bloody fantastic. Can you do it more often and for longer?" or "Instead of doing X can you do Y? I *love* it when you do Y!"

If that doesn't work, have a chat outside the bedroom. Start with a positive by saying how much you enjoy sex with them, then say you've noticed they don't seem to be getting the hint about what you do or don't like. Is there a specific reason why or did they just miss your cues? You want more oral sex from her? Could be she did get the message but hates you ejaculating in her mouth. Also look at what it is exactly that you're asking them to do. Is it a little out-there? Feeling miffed that your husband's refused your request for a foursome with the two hunky builders renovating the kitchen is a tad unfair. Some things you just have to relegate to fantasy land. (However delicious the idea might be...)

Stop Your Kids Killing Your Sex Life

It's ironic that the product of sex – children – threatens the very thing that brought them into the world. It's not just sleep deprivation that can turn a sexually charged couple into who-can-be-bothereds in under a week. But there are ways to stay both sane and sexual…

Let me give this to you straight: having kids might be the best thing you ever did but it's also going to be the hardest. Children put more strain on you, your relationship, and your sex life than you ever dreamed possible. "It's relentless – I had no idea it was going to be like this." "If I'd known, I don't think I'd have had one." This is what new parents really say after having a baby – the gushy "Yes, isn't she just gorgeous? I'm so lucky!" is purely for the little old lady who stopped to goo-gaa over the pram. Don't get me wrong: babies and children are adorable. So much so, your heart feels swollen to bursting point with the intensity of your love for them. But you know that. What people *don't* tell you is that babies and children are disruptive, destructive little buggers that can sense an erection, a cuddle, or an air-kiss that threatens to turn into a snog, within seconds. Then they do everything in their power (which, believe me, is immense) to thwart it.

When most couples picture having children, it's usually an image of holding a baby that's beaming up at them. Or playing in the park. What they don't imagine is the exhaustion, monotony, boredom, frustration, sleep deprivation, and nagging anxiety that never, ever leaves you. How you're both there purely for the children and your needs are secondary as your entire life gets reorganized around them. There's no spontaneity, no privacy, no freedom, no uninterrupted couple time. Parents with kids spend an average of 20 minutes per week being intimate. You have to rush everything. Is it any wonder that lots of parents wish they'd never had children in the first few years? So don't feel guilty if this is you!

A definitive study of 30,000 parents revealed most couples with children are less happy than couples without and the more children they had, the less happy they were likely to be. Women with children under one are the least happy (only 38 per cent highly satisfied compared with 62 per cent of childless people) but don't think the worst is over after the "terrible twos": the teenage years can be the most traumatic of them all. Having said that, once the child does reach two, parents start to feel a lot better about their relationship. And on a *personal* level, children are likely to make you happier rather than less happy. Some more good news so you both don't board that one-way, child-free flight to Mexico: couples who were happy before they had children appear to be relatively protected from most of the negative effects of having children. Even more so if the decision to have them was mutual. What is clear, though, is babies won't bring you closer if you're not happy to start with: having children to "save" your marriage is one of the most foolish, misguided decisions you'll ever make.

The most important piece of advice I can give you: go into parenthood knowing what you're in for. Make a pact from the start to face up to what's ahead *together*, to talk honestly, and to love each other as well as the kids. Those are the basics, now let's move on to the nitty-gritty…

What she's feeling

Women want their lives back
The overriding emotion is resentment. Her life is now utter chaos while yours seems sort of the same. There you are, feet up on the sofa, channel surfing as always. Just as she walks past with baby in one arm and dirty washing in the other, you chortle at a cheesy sit-com and she *hates* you. When she blearily and wearily gets out of bed to breastfeed and you roll over and contentedly snuggle back in, she hates you a little more. When your penis eagerly prods her in the back on the one day she could sleep in, she hates you so much, you're lucky she doesn't turn around and rip it right off with her bare hands.

Running snugly side by side with her anger and growing with equal intensity, is an overwhelmingly startling love for her child. People tell you you'll love your children but no one told her she'd fall *in* love with them. She used to be besotted with you, now she can't take her eyes off her child. All the caressing, squeezing, and kissing hasn't disappeared, it's just directed at the kids, not you. "In the physicality between mother and child lie a multitude of sensuous experiences," says US therapist Esther Perel. This all-consuming love doesn't just switch off during sex. Lots of women say they find it completely impossible to stop being a mum – one part of her is always listening, always alert to her child. Pleasure requires a healthy amount of selfish hedonism. And I'm afraid that disappeared the second your sperm sidled up to her egg and said "How about it?"

What she wants to say to you
The more you help me with the chores and kids and running around, the more energy and love I'll have left over for you. Sleep is more precious to me than sex right now, so the more sleep you can help me get, the more sex you'll get. Oh, and offering to hold the baby while I load the dishwasher isn't what I had in mind. And making the bed involves more than just pulling up the duvet.

What he's feeling

Men want their wives back
He's feeling abandoned. Your life used to revolve around him, now he barely gets a look-in. He doesn't just feel he's got a rival for your affection, he feels replaced. As one man put it, "She stopped being a wife once she became a mother." Then there's the whole "How can I have sex with the mother of my child?" thing: too much respect for Mummy, no matter how yummy, causes problems. He's already struggling with "erotic" and "wife", add "mother" on top of it and you – and he – have problems. If he saw you give birth, images of *what went on down there* are still churning uncomfortably around his confused head. Add images of the baby attaching its lips to breasts that were once only for his pleasure and you start to understand why it's not just you who has problems flicking the switch from "mummy" to "sex kitten".

If he manages to get through this quagmire of emotions and initiate sex, it's usually rejected. And not terribly nicely. That glare you shot him said "You insensitive *prick*! Can't you see how exhausted, stressed, unhinged I am already?" Thing is, as much as he wanted sex, what he was really after was attention. Reject sex and you're rejecting him as well. It's the one thing the baby can't give you that he can, so he feels even more useless than before if that's not on the cards. In fact, apart from the increasingly overwhelming financial responsibility of providing for everyone, what is his point exactly?

What he wants to say to you
I know this is hard for you but we're both getting a raw deal here – you're knackered, but since you became a mum I've lost my best friend and lover. So please act like you at least still like me, by giving me attention as well, and if you don't want sex that's fine but be nice about it. Don't glare at me and make me feel bad. I'm not an ogre for finding you attractive and sex would make me feel wanted and loved.

Stay sane

Don't compete for the "I'm worse off" award. It's hard for both of you so don't play martyr or try to score points. Instead, work together as a team.

Don't feel guilty about taking time out for sex and/or cuddles. The kids get your full attention the rest of the time, you deserve private time too.

Go out for dinner – just the two of you – at least once every two months. Drink lots. Get so drunk, you can't help but shag. Don't be the couple who only ever go out and have sex on birthdays and anniversaries.

Go to bed at the same time and sleep naked. Skin to-skin contact will keep the connection going.

Have a weekend away. Time away without the kids will rescue and rejuvenate more than you could ever imagine. If you can possibly swing it, do it. Everyone I spoke to said this kept them remotely normal.

Don't waste what spare time you have. Turn off the TV, get off the bloody internet, stop texting. Bed is a sex and sleep zone only: laptops and work are banned. Consider ditching the bedroom TV: those who don't have one in there have sex an average of eight times a month, twice the average of those who do.

Don't talk about the kids all the time. Remember what you used to talk about pre-kids? It's still interesting even if little Poppy is blowing bubbles with her juice. Read the newspaper – stay curious about life.

Don't replace your partner with your children. If you're not getting something you need, ask for it. Don't turn to the kids to provide it. Often they will and you'll be even further estranged.

Get and use babysitters. Bribe parents, siblings, your neighbours, friends… Cultivate a tribe of people you trust to look after your children.

Accept that things won't be perfect. Sex is going to be put on the back bench for a while.

Stay sexy

Keep cuddling even if you don't fancy sex. Hold hands, hug, swap air kisses for real ones. Have a bath together.

Have no-effort sex. If you're not feeling enthusiastic, let your partner masturbate while you watch. Perhaps even letting him finish by ejaculating on your breasts or tummy (come on, what's the difference between that and baby vomit?) Use a vibrator when you're too exhausted to have sex. Use it solo to keep your sex drive high (three minutes is possible to find when the baby is six months or older). Use it with him to guarantee you an orgasm during quickies.

Just do it. By the time you've dodged your partner's advances, pretended to be asleep, worried that you've hurt them by saying no, you could have had a quickie and both be sleeping with a smile on your face.

Bargain! This is fine in the early days; they get sex if they get up to do the early morning feed. It's totally acceptable to say "You've got five minutes" when they want sex but you'd cut your right arm off for sleep.

Plan sex. I've told you this a hundred times so far already in this book. And I'm telling you again. Create the right conditions – babysitter, time alone – or it isn't going to happen.

> Vanessa, 37, married five years
> **"Having kids made me a lot more confident, so while there's less time, I'm a happier person and *everything* is better! I feel closer to their father and not going out as much has its benefits: we have sex more because we're home more, so it's worked in our favour."**

Grab any sex you can. Don't be fussy. OK sex is better for your relationship than no sex.

Be creative. Send babysitters and their charges on trips to faraway shops for obscure ingredients, have sex on the sofa if the kids are asleep upstairs. Count "sexy" things as having had sex so it feels like you're doing it more: snogs, sexy massages, baths together.

Don't worry if you don't "finish" having sex. When was the last time you made a hot meal and managed to actually eat it while it was even slightly warm? Get used to it. It's how it is for a while.

Have a sex detox. If you're really finding sex a pressure, take it off the table completely for an agreed amount of time (no more than two months). Up the affection and promise each other sex is only gone temporarily. A "mental break" is sometimes needed.

Why warm sex will keep you hot

Warm sex usually involves you both playing with each other's bits but doesn't necessarily result in an orgasm for either of you – or even high arousal. You did it pre-kids: she'd get your penis out while you were watching TV, just to say hello, and stroke it affectionately. You either ended up with a raging hard-on or just relaxed into the nice feeling of "him" being loved. He'd idly caress your breast as you spooned on a Sunday morning, you half wanting to wake up to make love, half happy to just lie snuggling in that sleepy, sexy state.

Sex is "warm" when it is calm and less intense. It's the sort of sex you'll most probably have during the first few years of parenthood. Couples who value warm sex for what it is – a way of maintaining sexual connection, rather than seeing it as a "failed" sex session (not "hot" enough, no orgasms, frustrating) are the ones who are way happier sexually long term.

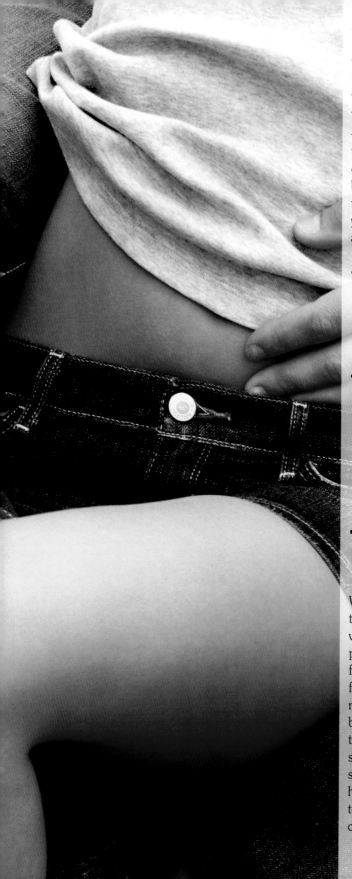

Will we ever get our sex life back?

That's the question I get asked most by new parents – always accompanied by the same freshly-clubbed-on-the-head, bewildered/vulnerable/panicked/exhausted expression. Sometimes, she'll add "Will I ever *want* it back?", in a tiny, miserable voice. The answer is yes to both questions. But not for a while, so brace yourselves. Statistics vary but the following will give you an idea of what's ahead (or what's not):

• Most couples don't have any sex at all for seven weeks after the birth. Lots don't start having sex until three months in, some wait up to a year. (Breastfeeding, by the way, appears to have no effect on the amount of sex the couple have.)

• About four months after the birth, couples usually return to however often they were having sex mid-pregnancy. Six months after the birth, most are clocking up three to five times a month. One year in, couples say sex is starting to feel good again, though few say it's as good as it was pre-kids. Post one year, 95 per cent of couples said they're still having less sex than before the pregnancy.

• A study of 11,000 men and women aged 16–44 revealed married women with kids under the age of five have the lowest libido of all the groups.

Women with small children are consistently most likely to report both short- and long-term desire difficulties, while men are the opposite, reporting fewer sex problems than single guys! There's a biological reason for her short-term disinterest: she's supposed to be focused on caring for her child rather than making a new one. There's also a biological reason for men being more up for having sex post-children, even if they are sharing the parenting load (yes, there is one such man but his identity is closely guarded). Both sexes produce testosterone, the sex drive hormone, but he produces 10 times the amount. More than enough to override the exhaustion, anxiety, and irritability that comes plopping out along with the baby.

What I've learnt so far...

To identify our relationship style and be acutely aware of both its strengths and weaknesses.

To face up to and fix our personal toxic lust killers. I can't have great sex if my relationship is in tatters.

To start saying yes to sex and stop making excuses for why I'm not having it. There are plenty of *great* reasons why I should be!

To adore and spoil my partner as much as I do my children. We need time together to play, as well as time to play with the kids.

To grab sex when we can, where we can, and however we can. So-so sex is better than no sex at all.

To accept that no matter how hard we think we've got it, our partner's life isn't as easy as it appears.

3
Not
Getting
Any?

Is Your
Marriage
Sex-Starved?

When was the last time you "did the deed"? Can't remember or don't want to and definitely don't want to talk about it? Then this is for you! Along with eight (sort of) easy steps to rescue the sorriest sex life, there's some pretty good reasons why you'd want to.

The second she walked in, I knew. A little late to arrive when she was always Ms Punctual, slightly breathless, new clothes, new hairstyle, a sassy little wiggle to the walk, a telltale glow to the skin, the sliding away of her eyes when I said, "You look fantastic! Have you had something done?" Or more accurately, "Who are you doing?" But she didn't confess and I didn't go there because I knew and loved her husband as much as her. Then I ran into him about a week later and thought, "Christ! What's the likelihood of them both having an affair at the same time?" Beer belly gone, cool jacket, hair all scruffy and sexy, sheepish but slightly pleased with himself look, naughty grin... What was wrong with these two!? It was so blatantly obvious they were both getting a bit (a lot) on the side – how could they not see what was going on?

I steeled myself for the inevitable, "We're separating because X or Y (whoever got caught first) is having an affair." But it never happened. After about four months, I tentatively asked her if things were OK. "OK?", she blurted out, clearly *dying* to confess. (Dear God, here it comes.) "My God, I've never been happier! David and I are having sex again and I've fallen back in love with my husband. And sex! *SEX!* Why did I stop having it? Why didn't you make me?" *Well, bugger me,* I thought, thankful I hadn't said it out loud. (How badly had I misjudged them! And given her new enthusiasm for sex, who knew what confession *that* comment might have led to!) Turned out, David and Sarah (yes, they're made up names) faced each other one night and said, "OK, we haven't had sex in four years. We either separate or do something." "Something" turned out to be a

How hot is your relationship?

Answer "true" or "false" to the following questions – and be honest rather than hopeful!

- Does one of you always initiate sex and the other feel pressured?
- Do you rarely or never have sexy thoughts or fantasies about your partner?
- Is touch and physical affection lacking outside the bedroom as well as in it?
- Do you rarely look forward to having sex?
- Do you feel little connection during sex?
- Is sex something you do more out of obligation than want?
- Does sex feel very routine, like you're both just going through the motions?
- Do you avoid having sex as much as possible?
- Are you having sex less than once a month?

If you answered "true" to more than five of the above statements, it's very likely you're struggling with low sexual desire.

brilliant sex therapist who sorted them out in no time. The clothes, the "new" bodies – she said it all happened as a consequence. Once they started having sex, they felt more confident, sexier, braver about trying new looks, and more motivated to look good. Two years in, they're still floating about looking fantastic, blissfully happy and, yes, still shagging like rabbits. They are one of my main inspirations for writing this book – and they're *your* inspiration for turning your love life around. It can be done. If ever there was a sex-starved couple, they were it. If they can do it, so can you. With one proviso. None of this will work unless you get rid of any festering anger and

If either of you dares to tell me you don't have time to fix your low- or no-sex relationship, I've got a few choice words for you: turn that sodding television off!

resentment. (If you don't know how, see page 53.) You have to at least like each other enough to try. If you don't, you'll fight each of these suggestions every step of the way, resenting every single one of them. You have to *want* to fix this.

Another thing: if you've struggled with low desire in your marriage for a while, you may have already done some research and heard some of this before. Great! But this time, can you actually try *doing* what's suggested, rather than just reading or talking about it? There's a reason why top sex therapists tend to settle on the same themes for this particular problem: they're techniques or mindsets that actually make a difference. One final point: if either of you dares to tell me you don't have time to fix your low- or no-sex relationship, I've got a few choice words for you: turn that sodding television off! There! Now, we're ready to start…

Eight steps to get your mojo back

01 Confront the problem

Tackle anger issues: Forty-four per cent of men in one survey said the main reason they weren't sleeping with their wives was the fact that they were *furious* with her. They felt "criticized, controlled, undervalued, and insignificant" in their relationships. If there's lots of anger and resentment over sex on either side, call a truce. Say, "I'm sorry we've been having hassles over sex, darling. I do love you and really want to solve this. Shall we work together to see what we can do?" If you think this would be about as effective as using a tissue as an umbrella – the situation's *way* past being fixed by an apology and a chat – see a therapist (see page 183–5).

Force yourselves to talk about what's going on: You can't shut couples up talking about sex when it's going great, then when you *really* need to talk – when problems hit – you're both quieter than a three-year-old discovering their mum's make-up stash. Hurt, tense, anxious – under these circumstances talking isn't fun but talk you must. (See page 134–142 for hints on how.) If you're seriously too nervous, buy a book that you think deals well with low or mismatched desire (this one for instance!) and I suggest you read it together. If you're too scared to do that, find a good therapist to do the talking for you (see pages 183–5).

Approach it as a couple problem that's no one's fault: Both of you are hurt and no one's "right" or "wrong". The person who wants sex more isn't "sexier" or "better". The person who wants sex less isn't "frigid" or the one with "the problem". If there's a desire mismatch – one of you feels rejected, the other feels pressured and hassled – it doesn't feel great on either side. Stop blaming each other and start working together as a team.

Should you solve your sex problems or relationship problems first? It's assumed you should deal with emotional issues first but most therapists don't separate sex and marital therapy. The thinking is this: if you analyse a couple's sex life, you get to relationship stuff. If you analyse their relationship, you get to the sex stuff. Just tackle *something*! If your problems with sex seem less daunting than the relationship issues, fixing those first could give you the confidence to tackle bigger concerns.

Susan, 42, now single
"My husband was asexual: unless I made a move, the thought of sex would never occur to him. After 15 years of trying everything, I left. I've had three lovers since and sex has been the main focus of the relationship. I don't care what people think, I'm making up for lost time."

02 Set realistic aims together

Look after your needs solo: Your partner's not a robot that you can programme to always feel like sex when you do. If only. Sexual frustration turns us into grumps so get busy with that hand. If you're a woman and don't have a good vibrator (really?), go online now and buy one. Use it often until the problem's solved.

Embrace the dreaded "C" word... compromise: If either of you is unhappy with the amount of sex you're having, try doing this: the high-desire person decides on the *least* amount of sex per fortnight they'd be happy with. The low-desire person decides on the *most* often they'd be willing to do it. Then you choose the number in the middle of the two. Making it fortnightly allows for life interfering with the commitment. Make it monthly and you forget what you promised. It's a good starting point. (Don't be surprised, by the way, if your estimates of how often you actually are having sex don't tally. The sex-starved person tends to dramatically underestimate, the hassled person thinks it's higher. Both of you distort reality.)

Talk about what you'd like to do in the sex sessions: Say what you most like and least like, though play nicely and focus more on the positives than negatives. How could you improve things that aren't working? Be specific about what you need and want. Talk about when you did have great sex. What made it work when it worked? What did you both do differently back then? How did you treat each other in and out of bed? What was different about your lives? Write down specifics and work out how to reintroduce the key elements. (How's it going at this point, by the way? I bet once you started talking honestly without worrying about being judged, you're astonished how everything suddenly seems fixable. Which leads me into my next point...)

Don't expect it to be solved overnight: After the first honest chat, couples often feel so liberated, uplifted, and relieved, it feels like everything is fixed *already* – just by talking! Don't get me wrong, you've just tackled the hardest part – admitting there's a problem – but there's still a little way to go before you start to see real results in the bedroom.

Vow to make the effort: Sexual boredom is a given in marriage, says David Schnarch, a top US sex therapist. He says lots of couples end up doing the "leftovers": "Whatever is left over when he says he's not comfortable doing that and she says she isn't comfortable doing the other." Depressing or what? What do you fancy? Making a meal, night after night, out of scraps or putting a bit of effort in and turning raw ingredients into a glorious feast?

03 Get fit for sex

Look the best you've ever looked: Hands up who needs to lose weight? The slimmer you are, the higher your self-esteem and the sexier you feel. Almost all people report an increase in their sex drive after losing as little as five pounds.

Move: Exercise boosts libido levels, makes you feel and look better, and also gets you "unstuck" in other ways. If you want to change someone's mind in an argument, get them to move from whatever position they're in. Changing position opens them to new ideas. Same applies to your relationship. Get it *off* the sofa and go for a walk together rather than watch TV. Wake up and go for a run or go to the gym rather than slob around drinking coffee.

Get a medical: Tackle any chronic conditions – migraines, back pain, a dodgy knee – that interfere with sex. For sexual problems like erection difficulties, vaginal dryness, and painful sex see your doctor (yes, you can – easy choice: slight embarrassment or a lifetime of good sex?). Take your regular medication into the doctor and ask if it could be affecting your sex drive. Anti-depressants, blood pressure pills, the contraceptive pill are all culprits. Ask for alternatives – consider switching to contraception that doesn't involve hormones (condoms, IUD, diaphragm).

04 Act on a mere flicker of lust

You sort of wouldn't mind if you had sex? Don't just ponder the thought, bloody pounce on it – and do it as soon as you can! Studies show the more time that passes between having an idea and following up on it, the more likely you are to lose motivation. I'm not saying you should burst into your partner's board meeting and drag him out by the tie, but don't let things like the dishes or the meal being ready or "I'll just answer that email first" get in the way.

Think of your sex life as a bank account: You need to make regular deposits to keep the balance healthy. If you've both just come back from a pleasant little shagathon in the Greek Islands (kids happily tucked up at Grandma's house), the balance is nicely topped up. Saying "No" to sex the night you get back isn't going to cause problems. But if you haven't made a deposit for six weeks or more, that balance is getting dangerously low.

Don't feel bad about faking desire: As I've made perfectly clear in the "duty shag" section (see page 88), it's childish to expect both of you to always be gagging for it simultaneously. Numerous studies show lots of us warm up once we get going. Besides, sex is like chocolate: even when it's bad, it's usually still pretty good.

05 Set a sex schedule

Make dates for sex: Don't just wait for it to happen. Find the whole idea of planning sex deeply off-putting? Think about it for a moment. Do you expect to be able to turn up to the best restaurant in town without making a booking? No. Does it put you off going once you've booked because you know it's going to happen? Quite the opposite. You think about it, anticipate what you'll eat, salivate at the thought of the first mouthful of that famous melted chocolate pudding.

We plan dinners out, holidays, and social get-togethers and look forward to all of them. So what's the problem with planning sex, then? The alternative to not scheduling sex is waiting for you both to feel like it, spontaneously, at a time when the kids aren't around, you're not both at work or exhausted, neither of you has an early-morning meeting… like, how often is *that* going to happen? As one expert put it, "Happy accidents don't happen regularly enough." So choose a point in the week when you have the most time, when

you are both able to properly relax and simply mark it as "us time". You can either leave it at the same slot each week or be more flexible and choose a new time or night once a week.

Now plan for it just as you would any big night out: What are you going to wear? Do you want it to be romantic or sexy? Raunchy or relaxing? Just as you try out new restaurants, try out new sex styles, techniques, and experiences. Take turns to plan the night with the only rule that the other has to be gracious and give whatever the other has planned a go. A little healthy competition is good – you'll both try harder – but resist the urge to criticize if you don't think they put as much effort in as you did last time, especially if you're naturally more sexually creative and confident. They did the best they could. If you're struggling to even remember how the hell the missionary position worked, let alone come up with new ideas, flick to chapter five and nick some stuff from there. The whole point of sex books is that people like me do the thinking and planning for you

06 Go out

Go out with friends together: Desire feeds on newness and seeing your partner in the company of others makes us see them through fresh eyes. And don't stick to the same old group of friends, mix it up! Say yes to any invitation that exposes you to different people and things (well, within reason). Don't be freaked if your partner seems "different" in different situations. This is a good thing! We try to turn our partners into someone who won't surprise us because surprises make us feel insecure. The downside: you're safe but bored senseless.

Flirt with each other: Are you snorting with derision? Listen, I was with you! Whenever I read this particular piece of advice I used to think, "Oh for God's sake, flirting seems so forced, so silly when you've been together forever." Until I studied a really happy couple I know and realized they've never *stopped* flirting. There it was, the extended, adoring eye gaze we all do at the start. Standing really close, giving *full* attention, kisses on the forehead, always touching each other. Yes, I hate them and feel free to as well! Lucky sods… Or is it luck? Maybe it's the flirting that's kept them in love? Give it a whirl.

Do exciting things: And I don't mean try out that flash new Thai place. Do shocking things to get your heart thudding. Jolt your brain into falling back into lust – any type of adrenaline-boosting activity drives up the dopamine level in your brain, making you feel lustier and more in love. Do things that slightly freak you out – ride a pushbike through traffic, kick-box, go on a rollercoaster, wear your hot-pink skyscraper wedges to the office. Apply the same rule to sex: if doggy style seems terribly risqué, do that. Or give your partner oral as he leans out the upstairs window to chat to the neighbours, leaving you hidden from view.

You sort of wouldn't mind if you had sex? Don't just ponder the thought, bloody pounce on it – and do it as soon as you can!

Why you've *really* gone off sex

Some things we'll readily admit to – you're exhausted, have small kids, your mother-in-law moved into the spare room. Others we don't dare say out loud because they sound (and sometimes are) unfixable. Like the fact that…

- **You've outgrown your partner.** You got married young with the same aspirations but while your partner plodded a predictable path, your career soared. Ten years on, you're horribly mismatched in achievements, incomes, lifestyles – and your new "ideal partner" is someone completely different.
- **You don't find your partner attractive** – on any level. I often ask couples, "If you met your partner now, would you fancy them or want to date them?" If the answer is an immediate and vehement "God no!", it's obvious the marriage is limping towards the finish line and that sex stopped a long time ago.
- **You want a baby** – and his sperm doesn't seem to be doing the job. Nothing kills the desire for sex more than being told you must have it. Trying for a baby is tedious. But it's also not unusual for women who've been told their partner has fertility problems to stop having sex with them and look elsewhere. You're driven by a primitive, irrational urge to search for healthy "seed" and end up having unprotected sex with a lover.
- **You have the baby so no longer need them.** One reason why children rob us of desire is that we get a lot of needs met by a baby. Unconditional love, cuddles, company, amusement. Babies provide a lot of entertainment and satisfy a lot of emotional needs. If you weren't that into your husband to begin with, he's pretty easily replaced.
- **You've had your fill.** Some people get to a certain stage and decide to close the door on sex. If you've never really been into it, hitting 50 or 60 sometimes means hitting your limit. You then refuse to have any sexual contact or reduce it to "special occasion" sex – or continue to have sex but enforce conditions: no kissing, no foreplay, no touching, just pure genital to genital contact. This happens more often than you'd like to think.

If you're going to say no...

- **Consider the consequences.** If your partner's horny, what are they going to do with that desire? Masturbate secretly in the shower or pull out the vibrator once you're asleep? Slip into the office to watch internet porn? Don't make your partner feel bad for doing these things: tell them to masturbate while you watch, let them know you don't mind if they slip off into the study to "be naughty". If you say no *regularly*, there are other consequences to think about… temptations such as strip clubs, sex workers, starting an affair. If you say no, make sure you know what you could be getting yourself into.
- **Have low-effort sex.** You're not interested in receiving sex but what about giving it? If you're practised at giving oral sex, deliver an orgasm in five minutes and both go to sleep happy.
- **Offer something else.** Reject sex but not affection and it won't feel half as bad their end. Tickle his back, comb her hair, give a massage – anything pleasurable that involves touching.
- **If you're going to say no, say when.** Let them know when would be a good time and then make sure you honour the promise. It doesn't need to be an hour-long marathon, but do offer something.

07 Make the first move

Whoever wants sex the least, needs to be the one who instigates it: The low-desire person sets the frequency because it's only when they give the thumbs up that sex happens. If this is you, turn the tables to be the one who suggests sex, rather than rejects it, and watch the dynamics change dramatically. Being the one to *want* sex, the one *asking* for it, instantly makes you feel sexier, more powerful – in charge. Your partner, who is used to being knocked back, will be both surprised and (hopefully) thrilled. Their ego gets a much-needed boost: maybe you fancy them after all! Maybe you like having sex with them! Maybe, just maybe, you want them as much as they want you… It's win-win for both. Try it.

Make sure the move isn't so subtle, they miss it: Especially if your partner isn't used to you initiating. What seems abundantly clear to you, may be misinterpreted by them – which is disastrous. You're left feeling confused (They're always hassling me, how come they don't want it now?) and confidence plummets (I feel silly suggesting it anyway so I won't do it again). All well and good to toss a sultry look as you head up the stairs to bed, but unless you're

...porting a leopard-print push-up bra, thong, and a garter belt at the time, "sultry" could be mistaken for "sulky" if he secretly feels guilty for staying up watching the football. If you're both shy or the sex situation is so tense that everything is likely to be misread negatively, have an agreed private code that says "Sex tonight?" Put two different magnets on the fridge and place yours high if you're up for it. Or do something cute with your toothbrushes before your partner comes in to clean their teeth, like make the shape of "Y" for yes.

Help each other get in the mood: Tune in to when you both most feel like having sex. After a good night out and a few drinks? After a good chat and a movie? Be honest and say what you need. Keep it light and say, "If you pour me a big glass of wine and massage my shoulders, I'll be a much surer thing." Or, "Can I have a bath for 20 minutes? Then I'll be much more in the mood." Get *yourself* in the mood: put on sexy underwear, run a tried-and-tried fantasy in your head, read a sexy book. Do what made you feel sexy the last time around. This sends a signal to your brain – "she's going to have sex again" – and triggers the right physical responses.

08 Change how you have sex

The longer you're together, the more "efficient" you'll be sexually: Sex becomes business-like and brief. You know each other's triggers and buttons to push and press them accordingly. Blindfolded, most of us could pick our partners within three minutes. We all have a certain style of kissing, a certain way of using our hands, tongues, and fingers, a certain way of thrusting and moving our hips. Now, while this may have reduced you to jelly at the start, 10 years in, even the most inattentive lover has figured out what's to come. (And it isn't going to be you, long term.) Repetition dulls desire.

The easiest way to transform your tired techniques is to buy a sex book packed with practical techniques (like this one, for instance) as a present *for the two of you*. Say it's to keep sex fresh, rather than to liven things

up. It's a subtle difference but an important one. One implies curiosity, the other boredom. Then each of you should mark one or two oral or manual techniques you'd like to try *on each other*. Choosing something that you'd like to do to your partner, rather than a technique you want them to do to you, will put a completely different spin on it. It's loving and giving and can't be interpreted as you being selfish or critical of their existing technique.

Slow down and take your time: Yes, you both know what's going to ultimately push each other over the finish line but deliberately steer away from it. Instead, learn to explore. Erection problems lessen if men can learn to take time over sex – there's less angst over an erection that goes up and down if you're not focused on his penis. (It's normal for erections to come and go during sex – it can happen two to five times in a 45-minute sex session.) The less penis-centric she is, the less he'll be. So take your time and meander sexually, exploring other body parts. Rediscover places like the neck. Remember how good it felt when you got kissed or bitten there? Stroke each other's backs and thighs.

One of my exes wouldn't (or couldn't – was never quite sure!) get an erection until he'd stroked me all over, looking at where he was touching, turning me over, and examining my body from every angle. At the start, it annoyed the hell out of me (*Hurry up for God's sake! I've got a huge day tomorrow!*) But once I relaxed into it, it never *ever* failed to turn me on big-time. By the time he finally conceded to put his hand/finger/tongue/penis where I wanted it the most, I'd orgasm in about two minutes flat. This lends new meaning to what your grandmother told you: good things come to those who wait. And those who wait, come harder and stronger.

Buy a book and say it's to keep sex fresh, rather than to liven things up. One implies curiosity, the other boredom.

The argument for "duty shags"

In today's politically correct climate, suggesting you have "duty shags" – have sex purely because your partner fancies it – is guaranteed to offend. We've all fallen prey to the "you should never do anything you don't want to" philosophy, so I'm fully expecting some of you to already be bristling with indignation. But, hell, someone's got to say it regardless of the consequences or we're all going to end up divorced, celibate, or so desperate the old man next door in the button-down cardi looks *hot*. So here it is: if you're in a long-term, monogamous relationship, I think you should accept that you will have to have sex when you don't feel like it sometimes. Maybe more than sometimes.

The argument for having sex with your partner, even if you're not drooling with anticipation, sliding off your seat, or frothing at the mouth for it, should simply be that you love them, value the relationship, and want to make them happy sexually. And because you know they would do the same thing for you. Let's be realistic here: you might not say "to love, honour, and shag" but that's what's implied when you make a commitment to only sleep with each other. You promise to satisfy each other's sexual needs on a reasonably regular basis. If either of you stop doing that, you can't expect your partner to be either happy or faithful. And vice versa.

I want to make something else abundantly clear at this point. By "duty shag" I don't mean say yes, roll your eyes, purse your lips, and lie there like a cadaver, checking your watch behind their back. It must be done gracefully rather than begrudgingly or it's pointless doing it at all. This means seeing, rather than ignoring, the naughty glint in your partner's eyes and acting on it rather than pretending you didn't notice. Grabbing the hand that creeps over to your side of the bed even when you're up to a really good bit in your book, rather than pushing it away or (worse) patting it in a patronizing "There, there" fashion. I want you to see

here's the clincher – I want them to see lust – or at the very least enthusiasm – reflected in *your* eyes. How is that possible if sex is about as appealing as getting up and cleaning the oven at 2am? Well, if you're not feeling sexy, think emotively instead: about how happy your partner is that they're about to get something *they* want. Think generously – "This is something I can give him or her." That will get you through the first bit, then who knows? Study after study proves that if you make the effort to *try* to get in the mood for sex, a lot of the time you actually end up feeling like it. Even if you don't, most long-term couples know each other's bodies well enough to press at least enough of the right buttons to mean it's not an *un*pleasant experience.

Desire isn't the only motivation for sex. Love, fairness, generosity, and wanting to make your partner happy are damn good motivators as well. If your entire sex life consists of duty shags, you're in trouble. But even couples who rate their sex lives as "highly satisfying" say around 20–25 per cent of their sexual encounters are done to please their partners, rather than themselves. Some therapists claim that only about 40–50 per cent of sexual encounters are mutually satisfying and good for both partners. (And I don't shut up about this.)

Sally, 32, married five years
"I've got a photo of us that was taken early on in the piece, when we were still in the 'at it like rabbits' stage. I'm looking at him like I'm going to eat him! I'm so clearly in lust, it's hilarious! I keep it on the fridge to remind me of how much I wanted him then. And it makes me want him now. It's so easy to forget how

What to Do if
He's Not Up for It

Popular opinion has women turning to face the wall
but more and more often these days it's men who are
trotting out the "Not tonight, dear" line. Why have men gone
off sex and what to do if it's happening to you.

It was pretty obvious to everyone that Mark and Lisa were soul mates. Even more obvious that they were best friends. What was known only to a select few was the truth about their sex life: it was, and always had been, dire. Mark isn't adverse to "having a bit", as he puts it, but given the choice between Lisa naked, on her knees and begging to give him oral, and a packet of Marlboros, a bottle of red, and a curry in front of the telly, he'd take the telly every time. Lisa, on the other hand, would cheerfully hand over the winning lottery ticket for one, single, perfect orgasm. Sex was, to put it nicely, not quite as frequent or satisfying as Lisa would have liked.

They'd make jokes about it in front of me, about her wanting sex and him knocking her back. All funny-ha-ha but enough awkward tension for me to say to him

privately, "Be careful. She loves you but you need to make an effort. Notice her. Try just doing it. It's sex. It's important." He shrugged. And did nothing. Meanwhile Lisa tried everything. Massages, sexy lingerie, porn, role-play, different positions, different locations, talking dirty, talking sense, weekends away, weekends in. She gave Mark 20 years to get turned on. Then she gave up.

Lisa's lover undresses her like he's peeling the wrapper off the most delicate, breakable, precious object in the world. He studies her for long minutes, trails a finger over her thighs, tummy, across her collarbone, just above her breasts. He gives her one, two, sometimes three orgasms before thinking about his own. She's deliriously happy – and dangerously close to leaving Mark. The last time I went to their house to pick her up

for a girly night, she was standing in the kitchen, bending down to adjust the strap on her shoe. Her hair tumbled forward, her bottom pointed skyward, and the slit-to-the-thigh skirt opened to reveal an expanse of long, lean leg. The whole effect was so goddamn sexy even their neutered dog was gazing in rapt attention. Mark was flipping through a tabloid. "How hot does your wife look?!" I said, a tad desperately (thinking, *look at her, say you see how sexy she is!*) "She always looks great," Mark said tossing a cursory glance. He then cocked an ear to the living room, said "Have fun you two. It's starting," and disappeared to watch the tennis. A husband about to lose his sex-starved wife.

Even if you don't have the ferocious sexual appetite of Lisa, even if you'd never take a lover, even if you only want sex twice a month, even if you actually went off it for a whole year when your firstborn arrived, years of him not wanting to have sex with you on a reasonably regular basis will leave you feeling demoralized, depressed, and deeply upset. *I mustn't be sexy anymore. He doesn't love me. I'm crap in bed. He's having an affair. He's secretly gay.* (Doubtful, by the way – only about 4 per cent of the male population is gay.) *He despises me. He's punishing me. I'm too fat. I'm not adventurous enough.* And the list goes on.

It feels bloody awful, and like it could go on forever. But let me give you the good news. First up, his low libido often has nothing to do with him not loving you or finding you attractive. Secondly, the infidelity rate of men in sexless marriages is no higher than the national average of men in all marriages (about 20 per cent). Thirdly, your situation isn't as uncommon as you think it is. When renowned US therapist Michele Weiner Davis, with 30 years of couples therapy under her belt, suggested 25 per cent of American men didn't want sex, the response was indignant fury. "It's America's best-kept secret," she said, refusing to back down. And Britain's, apparently. Relate, a UK counselling charity, reported a 40 per cent increase from the previous decade in the number of men claiming to have gone off sex. These weren't men with erection problems, these were men who weren't interested in getting one.

And guess what? Some people think it's *our* fault! That men's declining interest in sex has got to do with women's increasing enthusiasm. The old "lie back and think of England" girl was pretty easy to please. The *Sex and the City* supersexualized version expects good sex regularly. That's scary. You'd have thought us adoring what he's loved all along would make his heart swell with joy but turns out it just makes his penis shrink. Nearly one in five men are worried about performance and say they don't feel they've succeeded unless their partner has an orgasm. Given only 26 per cent of women report they always experience orgasm during sex compared with 75 per cent of men, that's a lot of disappointed men!

So contrary to popular opinion that has the wife in rollers turning to face the wall, it's often the *man* who decides to stop having sex in long-term relationships. We just don't hear about it because no one talks about it. He doesn't because he's embarrassed (society says all men should be up for it all of the time). You don't because you think it makes you look bad (you're a lousy lay, married to a closet gay, just not sexy anymore, etc). Look around your closest group of six girlfriends and I'll lay a wager that at least one has a husband also saying no. Most women will confess an affair to a close friend within two weeks of it starting but very few will offer up a sex drought as a topic of discussion. The glorious thing about women, however, is even if you are keeping your "sordid little secret" to yourself, you're far more likely to have researched the topic and read about it than he is. Even if he's the one with "the problem". Women are fixers. And this is why I've directed this piece to you, rather than the man in your life who is, probably silently and shamefully, suffering from low desire. Read it, absorb the information, try out the advice. The alternative is ending up in a Lisa-type scenario (and while the lover did sound divine, the messy divorce that followed wasn't).

You'd think us adoring what he's loved all along would make his heart swell with joy. Turns out it just makes his penis shrink.

Get him back in bed

Help him deal with stress rather than add to it.
Too much work and not enough play makes his penis feel very dull indeed. (British men are particularly vulnerable: studies say they work the longest hours in Europe.) If he's not coping at work, his self-esteem takes a battering – lots of men define themselves by their status (their job), the money they make (their job), and how well they perform in bed (affected by his job). If it's not going well, it's not uncommon for him to "numb" himself sexually.

One in five men generally say their libido is low because they're too stressed from work. Then they kill what little desire is left by doing what most of us do when stressed: self-medicating with alcohol. Excessive drinking affects the production of testosterone, the primary hormone responsible for our sex drive. Not surprisingly, the kick-on effect of all this is often depression. So he pops off to the doctor, who hands out anti-depressants and maybe some blood pressure pills, effectively wiping out any cravings that might have still been hopefully hanging around.

A common side-effect of anti-depressants and anti-hypertensive drugs is… you guessed it, a low libido. So choose your battles carefully. "Honey can you fix the

> **Candice, 32, married one year**
> **"You must sleep naked. That skin-to-skin touch is incredibly important, it reminds you that you're lovers not just good friends. Being in a different bed always helps as well. You can't help but think about sex when you're in a hotel room, whereas the bed at home can end up associated purely with sleep."**

dishwasher?" as he walks in the door at 9pm isn't going to have him tearing your knickers off with his teeth at 11. "You must be exhausted! Fancy a beer?" just might. Encourage him to exercise to let out frustration and talk problems through with you.

Stop trying to seduce him if it's not working.
Opinion sharply divides on whether you should be trying to tempt him back to sex by doing overtly suggestive things like installing a lapdancing pole in the lounge and serving dinner in nothing but your high heels. The reason why is that it works on some men and freaks the hell out of the rest. Will it work for you? It depends on why he's gone off sex in the first place. If it's because he sees you as a friend rather than a lover, shocking him into seeing you as a good old-fashioned sex object could well do the trick. If he's avoiding sex because of erection problems, the pressure of not being able to perform when you so desperately want him to could be absolutely disastrous. A "real man" would be rock hard if treated to what you're offering. If he's not, his sexual

confidence slides quietly through the floorboards. Another reason why this can backfire: one of the problems is sex is *too* available to him so pushing it in his face (perhaps literally) doesn't work. There's a reason why weight-loss experts advise us to fill the house with chocolates and cakes. The more readily available something is, the less we tend to want it. "We demand stability in marriage, then when we get it, we complain things are always the same," says US therapist and author David Schnarch, sagely.

Don't overreact to any erection problems. His penis isn't 18 anymore and he's fighting it all the way. He expects to lose his hair and develop a beer belly but no one really talks about what happens to man's best friend as he gets past 40. The first time he doesn't get an erection on cue is a sobering experience, even if he's not sober. Erection problems aren't the same as low desire but if he experiences one, sooner or later he's likely to feel the other as well, say the experts. (Only 7 per cent of young men report problems being able to keep an erection. It's 12 per cent by age 40, 18 per cent by 50–59 and 25–30 per cent by 60.)

> *His penis isn't 18 anymore and he's fighting it all the way. No one talks about what happens to man's best friend past 40.*

Erections don't happen as spontaneously post-40, he usually needs hands-on stimulation – so give it to him! Penises become more unpredictable as their owners age, more vulnerable to feelings and insecurities. So be attuned to his emotional as well as sexual state. Let him know you think this is all normal so he won't panic or get embarrassed. Embarrassment is often why he starts doing the whole fake yawn at bedtime thing, terrified you'll suggest sex, terrified he'll fail again. Until, eventually, he starts avoiding sex altogether, unless it's just with himself.

Talk before you get too upset about it. Or it will end up coming out as an awkwardly blurted, "Honey, why haven't you wanted to shag me in a year?" (See pages 134–142 for tips on how to talk about sex effectively.) Assume the chat will have a positive outcome rather than expect the worst – it will hugely affect how you deliver your message and his reaction to it. The more confident you are that what you're suggesting will be met with approval and excitement, the more positive you'll sound. And the more likely he is to think it's a great idea. Assume he's going to be offended, upset, or angry and you'll be nervous, tentative, and defensive – and likely to get the same from him.

Don't put words in his mouth however tempting it is. Most women can identify and express their emotions along with what they'd like done about the situation in under a minute flat. He'll still be on, "Well... I think I feel... I don't know, I guess it's... It's sort of like, what's the word I'm searching for? I think it's... No, that's not it..." 10 minutes after you've asked any question that includes the word "feel". If he's seriously struggling, it's OK to say "Maybe you feel frustrated/ hurt, etc.?" But try to let him talk rather than you say what you think is happening in his head. Talk about your feelings but don't claim to know his.

Ask for one thing at a time. Because women are so good at processing information and articulating thoughts, we'll often fire off 10 requests and possible solutions in the one chat. Meanwhile, he's back at point one while you're rattling off number eight. One of my exes demanded I restrict my points in any emails to him to "three points per email – and only one sentence each, in bullet point format". Yes, he was a bit of a nutter with the emotional maturity of a rather dim 16-year-old but I did get the message. You'll get a lot further if you break your ultimate goal down into steps and feed it to him piece by piece, rather than all at once. Also try to make the requests action based.

Say "I want you to be more sensual" and you might as well speak Swahili. Instead say, "I love it when you kiss my neck" or "If you don't feel like sex, would it be OK if you gave me oral sex sometimes?" Anything that's based on "do this" rather than "say this" is usually a winner.

Find out what turns him on. You already know the answer to that one, right? You sure about that? Our partner is often the last person we tell our strongest, core turn-ons because they're often slightly dodgy. Your favourite masturbation fantasy is a girl going down on you? Bet you haven't confessed that one to hubby. (Justification being, "Well I don't want it to happen in reality and he can't exactly turn himself into a girl, so why risk it?") Get him comfortable enough to share his closely guarded real sexual self, risk letting

His computer gets all the action

Internet sex has replaced real sex for an alarming number of men. Net porn is instantly accessible, invites him to view ever-inviting images without fear of judgement, and offers an endless supply of variety, 24 hours a day. Pretty hard to beat that, girls... the only thing that evens it up is he's just as threatened by our vibrator.

Lots of men see internet sex as a way to have imaginary sex without cheating on their partners. (Can't argue with that one given the alternative!) Others use it as fantasy fodder to spice up sex. (Again, I'm not seeing a problem. We do the same thing with sexy novels.) Some guys will share it, inviting you to watch it with them. (Why not?) And some use it to replace sex. And this is a problem.

Net sex is zero pressure – and that's tempting if you're having erection problems (you don't need an erection to orgasm) or suffering from performance anxiety. If you suspect your sex life has disappeared into the computer, let your partner know *you* know, in a light-hearted way. Ask "What does it provide that I can't" and, if you can, indulge the turn-on.

> *If a man's been with his partner 10 years, is aged over 40, and having sex three times a month, he actually isn't doing too badly!*

him see *you* emotionally naked and you're poised on the edge of *seriously* good sex. At the very least, you know each other's "flavour" and theme so you can…

Indulge the turn-on. Stop with the knee-jerk reaction, however offended you might feel. Our secret turn-ons aren't secret desires to do them. He fantasizes about being dominated by a sex worker? Pressing a hundred quid in his palm and dropping him off at the nearest brothel isn't what he's wanting. What he wants is for you to ditch the innocent white lacy underwear you thought he'd like, for a leather corset, stockings, suspenders, and a wicked pair of thigh-high boots. Acting on his true turn-on in some way makes him feel heard, so don't dismiss it as silly or "bad" (or funny, even if it's positively hilarious!).

If he's come up with something doable (as opposed to the usual threesome), do it. He wants you to shave your pubes in the shape of an arrow? Stifle the giggle and get cracking with the razor. He saw a red and black lace teddy in the window of the tackiest sex shop in Soho? Buy it. You'll only have it on for about 10 minutes so who cares if it's itchy as hell. While you're at it, ask what turns him *off* as well. He hates that perfume you just spent a fortune on? The way you say "Do you want to have sex?" in a disinterested, "I guess we should" fashion? How you look in your favourite pair of skinny jeans? Wear the perfume out with friends, rethink the way you initiate (but keep the skinny jeans – some things aren't negotiable). Think back to what used to do it for him in the past. Talking dirty? You taking your clothes off nice and slowly for him? Do you still do it? If you don't, do it again!

Let him know you notice that he's trying. Reward the smallest sign of progress and don't force him to go too fast. If he seems stuck, ask him what he needs.

Keep it light and positive, not accusatory or nagging. Take the pressure off by making it clear you're doing this together, it's not all up to him.

He's fine emotionally but nothing's working physically? Take a look at his lifestyle. Encourage him to cut back on alcohol, quit smoking, exercise, reduce stress wherever possible, get enough sleep. Get him to see a doctor if you think he may be suffering from low testosterone or may need a little blue pill.

Keep your mouth shut if you are tempted to discuss it with a friend. Believe me, you admitting your husband hasn't wanted sex for six months is hot gossip. She will be tempted to pass it on to her partner to make herself look good (he complains they only have it once a week) or to reassure (they haven't had it for six months either).

Stop doing more of the same

This insight comes from US therapist Michele Weiner Davis who specializes in low-desire relationships. And it's one of those things where you read it and think, "My God. I *soooo* do that!" Michele says when something isn't working, we try to fix it. If that doesn't work, we try again – but use exactly the same method. And keep on trying, doing more of the same but thinking "This time it will work, I just need to try harder".

Women nearly always try to solve things by talking. And talking. And then talking a bit more. We try talking when his eyelids flutter open in the morning, just before they close at night, and all the minutes in between. "We're convinced somehow it's the timing that's wrong. It's not. It's that talk doesn't work for him," says Michele. If whatever you're doing isn't working, stop doing it! Having the same conversation 50 times is hell, not helping. Instead, says Michele, think about how *he* would solve the problem. He'd probably take action, rather than talk about it. Follow his lead. Try a different approach.

What to Do if
She's Not Up for It

You vowed to forsake all others – now she's forsaken you.
What do you do if you've been erotically exiled? Figure out
what's going on in her head, that's what, then set about fixing
it in bed. Here's how...

One reason why lots of men find it hard to commit is they can't imagine being satisfied by having sex with the same woman for the rest of their life. But "settling down" does have perceived benefits. *Finally, sex on tap,* you think! *Someone who'll be there whenever I feel horny and who'll satisfy all my sexual needs!* No more trawling the bars, being rejected by snobby, stuck-up bitches who thought they were better than you. No more going home with only your hand for company. Maybe the whole commitment thing isn't so bad? You'd be guaranteed a nice, warm, *nude* body in your bed *every* night, ready, willing, and able to service you at whim. Maybe you've got enough notches on the bedpost and don't need a new girl every month (week, three days, half an hour)? So you take the plunge: move in, get married, promise to be faithful. And then the unthinkable happens: the person who is supposed to be a "sure thing" won't have sex with you anymore. You're not supposed to go elsewhere for it but you're not getting any at home, so your supply of sex has effectively been cut off completely. And unless she changes her mind sometime soon – which doesn't seem likely – it looks like it's been severed for life. You're castrated.

This is the stark and unwelcome reality for lots of men in long-term relationships. Despite dire warnings from the boys on the stag night saying blow jobs finish the second the ring goes on her finger, despite the sit-coms that persistently show him wanting sex and her avoiding it, somehow you never thought it would happen to *you.* Your wife or partner loves you! You used to have great sex! What the hell happened? Hurt, rejected, angry, lonely, frustrated, emasculated,

depressed, powerless, worthless, confused – name any adjective that describes feeling horrendous and add it to the list of emotions you're feeling right now if this is what's happening to you. It's a bloody awful place to be and you have my full sympathy.

Can I start by saying it's totally understandable and acceptable for you to feel all of those things. Can I also say it's pointless hating all women over it, because these days it's just as likely to be *you* saying no and her being put on an involuntary sex diet. (See pages 90–93.) I also want to reassure you she's probably not doing it deliberately, probably does still love you and find you sexy, and probably feels as bad about not having sex with you as you do not having sex with her.

There are many, many reasons why women stop having sex: some she can control but some she can't. People generally cope in sexless marriages one of three ways: around 26 per cent have affairs, one third actively try to solve the problem or head to a therapist, and a third resign themselves to a lifetime without sex. To be perfectly honest, I'd rather you go for the first option than the last (that's not to say I'm recommending it – see page 124). The sane thing to do is try for the middle one: to solve the problem yourselves or trot off to see an expert in the field to help if you can't. This entire chapter is devoted to exploring the issue you're

Score points by being soppy

There'll be brownie points galore if you suggest this super-soppy exercise called "heads on pillows", courtesy of US sex therapist David Schnarch. (Either that, or she'll think you're gay.) Both lie on the bed, your heads on the pillows, and simply gaze into each other's eyes for what will feel like forever – five to 10 minutes. Schnarch swears it's an excellent way to reconnect non-sexually, so you'll spend more time having sex. Give it a whirl! I did and despite an initial fit of the giggles, it really does make you feel calm, peaceful, and like you're merging with your partner. (And if she really does think you're gay, blame me.)

struggling with (the whole book is actually). Read the bit that's meant for both of you (see pages 78–88) as well as this, but also read the part that's addressed to women whose husbands don't want them (see pages 90–97). It will make you feel a whole lot better and a lot less bitter, putting you in the right frame of mind to understand some of the reasons why she's saying no…

Get her back in bed

Accept she's not deliberately refusing to have sex. Some women do withhold sex as punishment but most feel horribly guilty for not wanting it. Australian sex therapist Bettina Arndt persuaded 98 couples to keep daily sex diaries for six to nine months. The couples represented all age groups and stages in a relationship – and the results weren't pretty. Arndt found women's loss of sex drive to be a huge issue in a lot of the relationships. "Many wrote saying they can't bear what it's doing to their men. Women feel horribly guilty, which dampens desire even further," she says. Your partner's probably aware you resent her for not putting out. Arndt says the partners felt, "Duped, disappointed, in despair at finding themselves spending their lives begging for sex from their loved partners. They are stunned to find their needs totally ignored and it often poured out in a howl of rage and disappointment." Like, *hello!* If you feel even a tenth as pissed off as these guys, it's not like she's not going to notice.

Put energy into the relationship. It's a generalization but not a myth: she needs to feel satisfied emotionally before she's motivated to satisfy you sexually. The reverse tends to be true for men: you need to feel like your sexual needs have been taken care of before you'll make the effort to be lovey-dovey. As you can imagine, this has the potential to quickly turn into a rather nasty chain reaction if one feels the other isn't delivering. You stop being loving to her because she hasn't put out for a while, she stops putting out because you aren't terribly loving. The more effort you put into showing her you love her, the more sex you'll have. How she feels about you is critical to her sex drive and orgasm quota. If you're having major problems that aren't going away, seek counselling (see page 183–5).

Mike, 42, living with his partner for nine years

"I have a much higher sex drive than my partner but I mostly get my own way as I know what she can't resist. If she's tired, I'll run her a bath, bring her a big glass of wine – that nearly always puts her in a good mood. Then we snuggle on the sofa, and I throw in a shoulder massage or a back rub, then I'll go down on her. She loves oral sex so I lick her until she comes, then penetrate as she's still riding the wave of her orgasm. If your woman enjoys the sex you do have, she's going to want more of it."

Speak her language. We all have a "love language": how we best like to express our love and like it expressed to us. For some people, it's touch. For others, it's words. Or presents. (Pray hers isn't the latter.) Work out what means love for her, then deliver it. Relationships survive when each person figures out the other's love language and speaks it, even if it's not their own. If hers is words, tell her you love her more often. If yours is touch, ask her to touch you more.

Do more around the house. She's tired from juggling too many balls – a prime reason why she's not interested in going anywhere near yours. Yes, I know we're better at multitasking but if she spends all day at work and all evening running around after kids, cooking, cleaning, and making duty phone calls to your mum, she's unlikely to disappear in the millisecond she has to herself before bed to emerge in a nurse's outfit, ready to role-play.

Notice her. And notice other men noticing her ("That guy totally checked you out then!"), particularly if she looks a little less, well… hot, than she did. Whether it's having kids that changed her body shape or relaxing into a comfortable, dinner-on-laps-in-front-of-the-telly long-term relationship, that single girl gym bunny who pounded the treadmill five times a week has run away. And believe me, she's more upset about waving goodbye to that taut, toned hot bod than you are. If she doesn't think she looks good, she won't feel like having sex. It's that simple.

So load on the body compliments and if she's struggling to lose weight, suggest you both go for a run/go on a health kick/join a gym together. Just don't ever suggest she's fat or needs to lose weight or she'll never speak to you again (tempting) or have sex with you again (not so tempting). Always disguise "please slim down" requests by using the "let's get healthy" angle. Even if she guesses what you're really saying, it's not been said. Her dignity is intact.

Stop hassling her. Nothing, but nothing, kills her sex drive more effectively than you turning *every* innocent air-kiss into a tonsil-tussle, *every* affectionate hug into an octopus-like lunge for her breasts, hands sliding up her jumper from all directions. I know you're so desperate for sexual contact you feel you have to grab it while you can. But you're *lessening* your chances of getting any by doing this. It's *intensely* irritating to be groped and if any and all affection is interpreted by you as "Let's go for it honey!", she'll simply stop touching and cuddling you at all. She might chuckle at the "all men just want women for sex" jokes in the sit-coms, but she's not laughing if she thinks you really do think of her that way. Groping isn't getting you want you want. Stop it.

Separate sex and affection. Tell her from now on, a hug or caress will be just that. No hidden agendas. Then stick to it, even if that erection is threatening to burst buttons. Agree on clear signs for initiating sex. In the bit written for both of you (read pages 78–88), I've suggested things like using magnets on the fridge. You can also agree to just come out and say "I really want to have sex with you. What do you think?" I don't really

care how you communicate it, so long as she's not feeling hassled when you're *not* actually hassling her!

Have the dreaded talk (yes, you must). Read pages 134–142 for general tips – and, by the way, don't be surprised if you don't get the response you're expecting and she thinks *you're* the one with the problem. The person who wants sex the most *always* thinks it's the other person's problem for not wanting sex as much as they do. Surprise, surprise – she may think it's your fault, not hers. She's not undersexed, you're *oversexed!* Let her know sex for you isn't just about the physical release, it's a way of getting close to her. Pitch it as you craving intimacy as well as pleasure. Also let her know she can be honest about what she wants from sex too. Does she enjoy having sex with you when you have it? Brace yourself boys: the answer might not be what you want to hear. If she's not happy, ask her to show and tell you what she does enjoy.

Support anything she wants to try to fix the problem. Her best friend swears peppermint tea helped to boost her sex drive? Even if you think it's a bonkers idea (and yes it is), go along with it. Who knows? It might work. If it doesn't and you've been supportive, she'll ask you to help her. Then you can suggest your far superior plan. Be patient. Don't make the mistake of thinking it's not working if you're not shagging like teenagers within a week. Notice every tiny step she makes and let her know you appreciate it, boosting her confidence along the way.

Get her to agree to have sex when she's *remotely* in the mood. And let her know that she can say no at any point. Frustrating if it's when you're just about to say "Ohmigod, I'm c…." and you haven't for about six years, but it will pay off in the long term. Lots of people, particularly women, don't get turned on until they start getting stimulated. On that note, both have realistic expectations about sex: it isn't endlessly mind-blowing. "Good enough" sex is good enough.

Get medical help. If she's perimenopausal, constantly hormonal, suffering from desire dysfunction, or sex is painful, encourage her to see her doctor, gynaecologist, or a sex therapist. (See pages 183–5 for more on this.)

Women are very good at saying "Oh no, I couldn't possibly do, that!", when they're secretly thinking, "God, that's so hot! Please let him make me."

Give her filthy sex. Women have less incentive to have sex than men do. It takes longer for us to get aroused and orgasm isn't guaranteed, so there's less motivation to make the effort if we're not gagging for it. (Could *you* be bothered if you didn't think there would be a happy ending?) So she wants to mix things up to make sex more appealing just as much as you do! It's just that when it comes to naughty sex, women are very good at saying, "Oh no, I couldn't *possibly* do that!", when they're secretly thinking, "God, that's so hot! Please let him make me." It's all about worrying you'll judge us if we admit to wanting filthy stuff. Christ, we won't even admit it to ourselves half the time!

In one experiment, men and women were shown various clips of sex including straight, gay and masturbatory sex – and even apes shagging happily for the camera! Both sexes were wired to measure arousal and asked to say how they felt. The results for men were predictable (both their heads and penises loved the "acceptable" stuff). But the results for women were astonishing: almost as though their mind and genitals didn't belong to the same person. They admitted being aroused by the "acceptable" choices but results showed they were rapidly aroused by pretty much *all* of the footage. Conclusion: she's up for a lot more than she admits!

Yaritza, 32, currently single
"Being Brazilian, sex is a very important thing. Among my circle of friends, the main cause of divorce is often related to sex – as in the lack of. There's even an urban myth that in Brazil, if the woman was a virgin and got married, she and he could cancel the marriage if they didn't like each other in bed within 24 hours."

What I've learnt so far...

To have sex more often even if I'm not particularly in the mood, to keep my libido purring and my partner happy.

To look the best I can so my partner loves the outside of me as much as they do the inside.

To make dates for sex rather than wait for it to happen. That way we both have something to look forward to!

To instigate sex more often so I feel powerful and sexy and my partner knows I enjoy it as much as he does.

To think of my sex life as a bank account: I need to make regular deposits to keep the balance healthy.

To stop thinking it's "their" problem if they want sex less or more than I do. We both have different libidos, it's no one's fault.

4
Get the Sex You Want

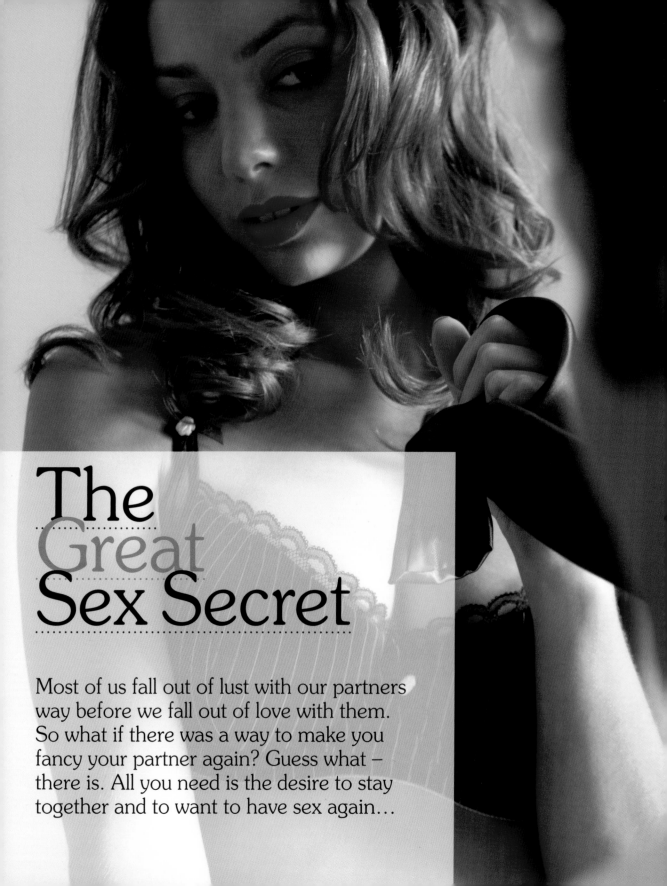

The Great Sex Secret

Most of us fall out of lust with our partners way before we fall out of love with them. So what if there was a way to make you fancy your partner again? Guess what – there is. All you need is the desire to stay together and to want to have sex again…

"I just don't fancy them anymore – if I did, I'd want to have sex with them." "I never feel like sex now and I used to have a really high sex drive. It's gone. Maybe I've just hooked up with the wrong person." "Our sex life is over. I never get that stirring in my lower belly. I used to get turned on just by looking at him." How many times have you heard people say things like this? How many otherwise happy couples do you know that have split because they no longer "fancy" their partner? Now, what would you say if I told you it's completely in your control whether you desire your partner or not? That it's entirely possible to resurrect sex and enjoy some pretty damn good sessions with them again – if you want to.

I suspect you'd say "bollocks" (that's putting it nicely). But this is exactly what the world's top therapists and fresh, challenging, new research indicates – and it goes against everything we've previously thought. Rather than subscribing to the "married sex just gets boring – deal with it" philosophy, these researchers believe good, satisfying sex long term is a *choice*. Desire is simply a decision and all it takes is an adjustment to our thinking. It's the great sex secret that no one's told you about… until now.

Most people think "desire" means "the urge to have sex". In fact, it can be *any* motivation that leads to the decision to have sex. Sometimes it *is* the biological push for pleasure that we commonly think of as "desire" – an animal urge to merge that magically springs up spontaneously (for him, literally) at the start of relationships. But what happens when you've "worn out" your sex hormones and desire is no longer instinctual and primitive? Well, according to experts, it's entirely possible to manufacture desire by

> ## James, 48, with his partner for 12 years
> ## "We met late in life and made a pact to see the good side of a long-term relationship and enjoy sex, rather than join in with the 'married sex is boring' jokes. We're still ridiculously happy 12 years on."

paying attention to other motivations for sex. In "The argument for duty shags" (see page 88) there are some good examples: loving your partner, wanting to make them happy. But there are some nicely selfish (far more persuasive) motivations as well: orgasms for starters!

Sex is a bit like smoking in reverse. Every smoker in the world would love not to *want* to smoke. Every healthy (sane) person in the world wants to *want* great sex. No one puts up their hand and says, "God, over here! Oh

please pick me!" when he's handing out the "will hardly *ever* want it" side of sex drives. We'd *all* love to *want* to shag our partners senseless 10 years on. The "want" is usually what's missing long term and causes the problems because, without it, there's no motivation. Which is why we all just sit on the sofa watching telly. Well, get set to press the "off" button on the remote because you *can* create this desirous state, one of two ways: by starting to actually have sex or creating the perfect conditions for you to personally get turned on. All you need to do now is pay attention.

Have sex to want it

Most of us think of sex as following this format: you feel like it. You talk your partner into it. You do it. This is based on a model the famous sex researchers Masters and Johnson came up with in the 1960s. On a graph, with the "time" line running along the bottom, the desire curve makes a rather pleasing breast shape. It starts at zero and climbs steadily through the arousal and a "plateau" period (you hover in the "good bit" for a while), peaks at orgasm (forming the nipple), then falls gently back down to "resolution" (the panting, recovery stage). It was a simple formula that *seemed* logical and still is – for most men.

Rosemary Basson, a physician in Vancouver, saw it differently for women. She'd seen clients that, rather than wait for the mood to strike, made themselves in the mood merely by "getting sex rolling". Once their body was turned on, their head followed – the reverse of how it is for most men. I have to admit, I'm with her, having both recent and personal proof for the "ass-about" theory: there I was the other night, watching a DVD with my boyfriend, (rather a) few wines in. Add an early morning the next day to the snuggly, sleepy mood and I had *minus* zero incentive for sex. I staggered into the bedroom, pointedly ignored the hopeful look thrown my way... and one hour and three orgasms later, he was begging *me* to go to sleep. "God, I'm too tired for this" rapidly transformed into "*Ohmigod* that feels amazing" with the lick of a tongue. The desire to have sex certainly wasn't there when I climbed into bed but it sure as hell was once we got going.

Basson's theory is there's more than one model of desire. Men are more likely to follow the original model and feel "spontaneous" desire – the "want it, then seek it" variety – while women's desire is "receptive" – they get mentally turned on by being physically turned on. This might not sound terribly exciting or significant, but for low- or no-desire women (and some men – this model isn't completely gender exclusive), it's the sexual equivalent of inventing the wheel. It means you're not boring, "frigid", or cold after all – *you simply get turned on in a different way!* You can be as horny, hungry, and sex-crazed as your always-up-for-it partner: you just get there a bit later on in the session, that's all.

If you had to do it...

The second way to create desire for your partner is to make sure things are as close as they can be to the "perfect" sex conditions for you. It sounds weird but think like this: if I *had* to have sex, when would I rather do it? This might be when all the chores are done and you can finally relax. When your favourite TV show's over but before you go to bed. It might be when you've come home feeling a bit tipsy. (It won't be the best sex you've ever had, but quite frankly, who cares if it's fun and you enjoy it!) It might be after you've had a laugh with your partner and are feeling generous. Or you've just watched her check the kids are OK and had a little stab of "Ohhhh, I do love her". All of these can put you in the right head space to being open to suggesting and having sex. Then it's a matter of building on that feeling – as illustrated by these steps:

Step one: What put *you* in the mood? Enough sleep, lots of affection, having a "skinny" day, actually getting home before 8pm for once, knowing the kids are safe at your mother's, a meal that didn't leave you with a tummy full of wind? (More people knock back sex for this reason than you realize!) Know – and let your partner know – what you need and do your best to make these things happen as often as possible.

Step two: Think of three good reasons why you should push yourself to have sex, even if you don't feel like it. It might be "This is too good an opportunity to miss".

Or "He's/she's really up for it and I want to make them happy". Or even "If I do it now, they'll let me sleep in tomorrow". (They don't have to all be politically correct, "nice" reasons! Just good motivators.)

Step three: That's put you in the right frame of mind, now take it to another level. What are your personal erotic triggers and turn-ons? It might be reading or watching something sexy, remembering former hot sex sessions, having a bath, being massaged. Make these things happen too, regularly. (Don't worry, by the way, if you're still not feeling "turned on" in the traditional sense at this point. Just keep moving forward.)

Step four: Initiate or agree to being stimulated sexually by your partner. Again, know what does it for you technique-wise and what doesn't and make sure your partner knows. If the technique is good and you let yourself relax into the sensation without pressure, you may well feel desire build as you continue.

Now, this plan isn't foolproof but I *guarantee* if you stick with it, your sex life will improve remarkably within a month. Couples have more sex on holiday than at any other time of the year. Why? Because they've created the perfect conditions for sex. You're relaxed, spending time together doing cool things, nicely rested, making an effort to enjoy yourselves, and taking advantage of spare time to enjoy sex. It works. Do it. To help you identify your erotic triggers, I've come up with a list of sexy things you can do for each other. Give them a go and let your partner know what did it for you and what didn't. The more you try, the better you'll know your personal turn-ons. Start by choosing one a week each to wake up your sleepy libidos, then up it to two a week (each) once you've got the hang of it. Then wait for those feelings you thought had gone forever to reappear. Yes really.

Couples have more sex on holiday than they have at any other time of the year. Why? Because they've created the perfect conditions for sex.

Get Him Hard

01 **Feel him up in public.** Choose a restaurant that has long tablecloths, unzip him, and deliver a discreet but delicious mini-hand-job (minus the happy ending, obviously).

02 **Snog him sexily in front of his friends.** Makes him look and feel like a Rock God, and his friends see how much you want him.

03 **Let him see you.** He's a natural voyeur so choose positions where he can see your breasts bouncing up and down. Let him open your legs wide to see your vulva before giving you oral.

04 **Put your fingers inside yourself** while he's watching or let him insert a vibrator, a dildo, or some love eggs. Men like seeing things disappear inside – and it's not just his penis.

05 **Muscle up** while he's inside you. Clench your pelvic floor muscles *hard*, grab his buttocks, and pull him close. Take over the thrusting and up the speed as you lean in to give him a deep tongue kiss.

06 **Get naked in the changing room.** Get him to wait outside the fitting room while you try on clothes, then invite him in after you strip off. He's fully clothed, you're naked – you can get away with him giving you two minutes of oral before the shop assistants get suspicious.

07 **Leave filthy photos in places where he least expects them.** Use a Polaroid to take up-close-and-personals. And I mean up close. (To us, it's not pretty; to him, it's an oil painting.) Tape one of the photos to the bathroom mirror as he's having a shower and then wait for him in the most brazen pose you can live with.

08 **Let him know you lust after him as much as he lusts after you.** "I'm never convinced she really enjoys it" is something men tell me all the time. Make noise, move, hire a plane to stream a message across the sky – let there be no doubt!

09 **Do a "Paris"** and tape a sex session. If you don't want any evidence hanging around, erase it once you've recorded it and had a little peek at the results. Half the fun is performing for the camera!

10 **Invest in some "slutty" stuff** purely for wearing at home for him. Skyscraper stilettos, tops slit to the navel, skirts so short you might as well just be wearing a thong…

11 **Leave the blinds up** as you're having sex. He doesn't know you chatted with the neighbours on their way out to dinner 20 minutes ago.

12 **Play the no panties game.** It's especially effective if you flash or tell him you're commando in situations where he can't ravish you. Go to the bathroom at that stuffy dinner party, take your panties off, and discreetly, under cover of the tablecloth, push them into his trouser pocket when you sit back down again.

13 **Make out in the back of a cab.** Up to you how far you go – the kick is in knowing the driver is secretly watching in the rear-view mirror. Open your legs wide (knickers on) and let him put his fingers inside you and he'll love you forever. True, the cab driver knows what you're doing but he can't see anything but a bit of inner thigh because his hand and your knickers cover the rest.

14 **Pretend to be a lipstick lesbian** next time you're out at a cool bar. Choose the prettiest girl in the room and tell him exactly how you'd lure her into your bed and what you'd do with her once there. He could (of course) watch.

15 **Tempt him at the traffic lights.** Pull your skirt up, take his hand, and put it between your legs or inside your top to run his hands over your breasts.

Don't ask for sex, just take it. Skip the niceties, grab him as soon as he walks in, get him naked, then do whatever you fancy.

Get Her Wet

01 **Tell her your most wicked and dirty thoughts about her.** Whisper them as your hands do what you're describing. Make sure there's no eye contact or pressure to talk dirty back so she can pretend not to like it (don't ask – it's a girl thing), despite the fact that she's gone pink with pleasure.

02 **Take her underwear shopping** to a stylish lingerie store. Tell her she can pick out two sets – but only if she models 10 for you in the fitting room. The classier the store, the less likely they actually are to interrupt the "viewing".

03 **Shave her legs for her** slowly and meticulously. She sits or lies on a towel, you sit beside her with a bowl of water, razor, and shaving foam. Let your slippery hands glide up and down her thighs, briefly brush but don't linger between her legs, push her thighs open under the guise of trying to reach a certain bit, leaving her exposed. Lots of looking and caressing but no touching of the naughty bits equals one *very* excited girl.

04 **Slide on a vibrating penis ring** before penetrating her. Grip her hips to hold her close so the little vibrator stays glued to her clitoris, then grind and rock against her instead of thrusting.

05 **Push chocolates inside her,** then lick and play with them with your tongue, coming up occasionally to give her deep, wet tongue kisses.

06 **Blindfold her** with a soft scarf, get her to lie back, and tell her she's not to talk but she has to do everything you say. Then give her orders like "Open your legs" or "Play with yourself". The blindfold removes eye contact making it less embarrassing, telling her she can't speak means she can't argue with you or answer back.

07 **Behave like a caveman.** Pick her up, throw her on the bed, pull her to you, and penetrate, grab a handful of hair as you're thrusting and pull it, bite her neck and breasts. "I wish he'd just go for what he wants rather than be so tentative" is a common female complaint. One you'll be happy to hear!

08 **Go down on her in an empty car park.** She stands, you pull her knickers to one side. It's easy to get away with if you stand between cars (but first check for sensor alarms on cars and security cameras!).

09 **Push a slim vibrator or vibrating egg inside her,** then work on her clitoris with your tongue for an orgasm she won't forget in a hurry.

10 **Put her over your lap,** pull down her panties, and spank her. Alternate spanks with running your fingers between her legs, licking them first.

11 **Feed her fantasy** about being seduced by a workman who's come to fix something (yes, some of our fantasies really are that clichéd!). Talk her through how you'd seduce her, why she's so hot…

12 **Have sex on a rug in front of a fire.** (Yup – that one too!) Ply her with alcohol, feed her sensuous treats, take her clothes off slowly, lick everywhere, take your time.

13 **Look at and explore every bit of her** with your eyes as well as your hands. There's nothing sexier than a guy obviously admiring and lusting after every inch of you, turning you over so he doesn't miss a thing…

14 **Send her a sex text when she's having lunch with her girlfriends.** "I want to be inside you." "I wish I was licking you right now." If she boasts there and then, you'll look good.

15 **Invite her vibrator into bed with you.** Ask her to show you how she uses it, then stop her before she gets too excited. Slide yourself inside her, then you or she hold it on her clitoris as you let loose (she's going to come in two minutes flat).

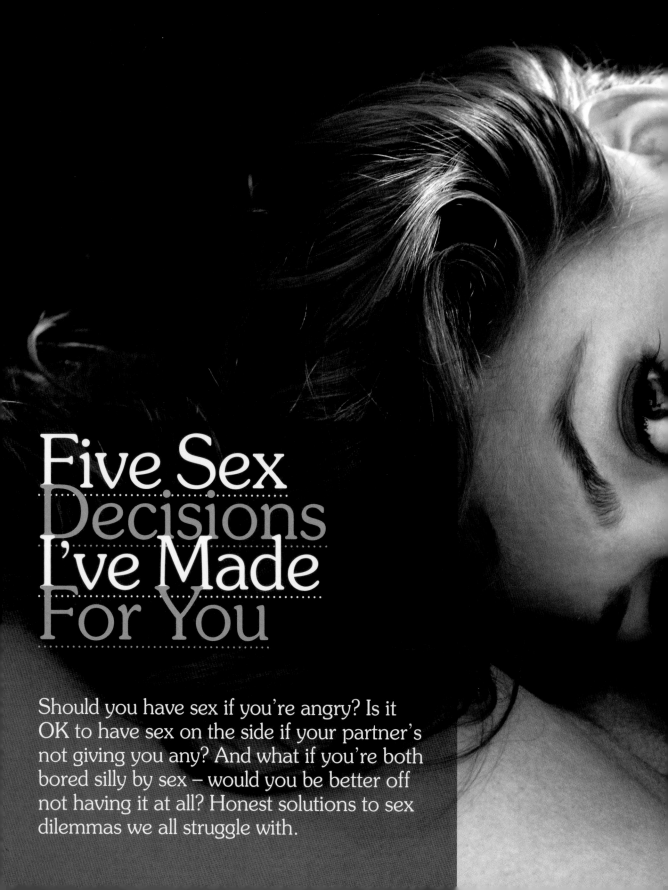

Five Sex Decisions I've Made For You

Should you have sex if you're angry? Is it OK to have sex on the side if your partner's not giving you any? And what if you're both bored silly by sex – would you be better off not having it at all? Honest solutions to sex dilemmas we all struggle with.

01 I'm so tired. Should I have sex or sleep?

It depends why you're so tired. If you're just knackered out by the daily grind of life, you're better off having sex. If there are babies involved or you're going through a stressful period that won't last (such as a promotion or death of a parent) you're better off sleeping. When the body is truly exhausted, our desire for sex shuts down to conserve the little energy we have left for more essential needs – like pumping blood around the body. Snuggle up instead with a promise of sex when you're both rested. But if you're just in that too-tired-to-be-bothered mode, making the effort to have sex yields all sorts of benefits.

Sex not only gives you energy (any exercise does, that's why you're better off going for a walk than having a kip a lot of the time), having an orgasm will make you sleep better afterwards. It makes you feel more connected to your partner and reduces stress levels, making you feel calmer generally. You don't think of sex as something you do for your health (though it's a brilliant excuse if you're caught doing it with someone you shouldn't be!) but it has tremendous health benefits! Regular sex triggers release of the hormones oxytocin, testosterone, and dopamine, lifting your libido, making you want to cuddle your partner, and making you feel happier. Sex is a natural antidepressant and good for bladder control. But the most persuasive reason of all is that having it tonight will make you more likely to want it the next time you're "too tired".

One study showed couples forced to have regular sex increased their desire for each other quite dramatically. They created a desire for sex that wasn't normally there! Higher libido people generally have more energy than lower libido people, so creating the have-it-want-it cycle can also make you less tired in the first place! Try this exercise to beat the too-tired-to-do-it rut: double how often you're having sex now. Then double it again in three months. Then again in six months.

02 Do I have to give oral sex?

Yes. Let me say that again unless I wasn't perfectly clear: yes. This is the one area where I'm not just putting my foot down, I'm stamping it. Refusing to give oral sex to your partner isn't just taking away a *hugely* satisfying part of sex – for women often the *only* way to orgasm – it rejects the *core* of a person. Call it "disgusting" or say you don't like doing it and you might as well say, "Your genitals disgust me. I don't like how they look and I don't like how they taste." If your partner refuses to give you oral sex, ask why. Worries over smell and taste are easily fixed by having a shower first, washing properly, and getting treatment for any infections. Worries over not really knowing what to do "down there" are fixed by an instructional sex session, giving clear and specific direction and feedback. Worries over "choking" are fixed by him not pushing the back of her head and her using her hands and choosing a position to control how deep he goes.

Worries about swallowing are fixed by stopping before he does and finishing him off with a hand. Worrying that it's "bad", "dirty", "wrong" are fixed by reading some good sex books to develop a healthy attitude and/or seeing a sex therapist. I think that covers the main complaints and – *surprise surprise!* – they're all fixable! I have yet to come across one person who has a justifiable excuse for not giving oral sex. (The closest was a woman who could only open her mouth about half an inch.) There *is* no excuse. Sort it out. Work out why you or they don't like doing it and do whatever it takes to solve the problem. Even if you don't particularly enjoy doing it, it's something you do to give your partner pleasure. Turn it into a gift.

Oral sex is the most intimate part of sex – you're taking your partner's most private part into your mouth. Relish in the taste, texture, smell, and experience of getting as close to them as possible. Show total acceptance. Be generous. And make sure you're good at it: it's one act where technique, experience, and skill count for a lot. (There, that told you!)

Should I have sex if I'm angry?

Enthusiasts of "make-up" sex will be jumping up and down saying "*Hell* yes!" but if you're not a fan, you maybe should be because sex when you're angry can be quite a good idea. Giving in to having sex, if one of you tries it on as a "make-up" gesture, can soften you towards each other and make you connect enough to talk calmly afterwards and fix the problem.

Now, if you're *mightily* pissed off with your partner, this is a bit like suggesting you invite the girl who shagged your husband at the office party to Christmas dinner. But if you're annoyed but not *that* pissed off, "parking" the anger for a little while isn't going to do either of you any harm. Try it. Even if you can't help prefacing taking your knickers off with, "This doesn't mean I'm not angry with you and don't hate you. It just means I still love you and value our sex more than the argument we've had."

US therapist Jack Morin says anger can be positive sexually, despite the fact it's such an unpleasant emotion. The primary function of anger is self-protection – we feel angry when we're feeling threatened or in danger. Thing is, risks and danger in the erotic context usually spell arousal. That's why forbidden sex is usually very good sex – doing something you're not supposed to has a certain "up yours" quality to it. Have sex in a park or with your boss and you're saying "Sod you!" to the authorities that say it's against the law or company policy. "It's a key emotion behind sexual acts or fantasies of defiance and rebellion," Jack says.

Some angry couples who fight lots *rely* on clashes between them to add drama to their sex lives. It certainly can act as an aphrodisiac. Jack's convinced one of the reasons couples have great sex when they're reunited after time apart is because there's subconscious resentment at the pain of being separated – especially on the side of a partner who suspects they missed the other more intensely.

04 Is it fair to get it elsewhere?

Fair is probably pushing it but it is understandable. This is commonly known as an "unmet needs affair". We say no one's perfect but if your partner's not meeting an important need like sex, what do you do? Go outside the relationship for it and it's a betrayal. Leave someone you love just to get that one need met and it seems like an awful waste. At this point you have some serious choices to make: continue getting sex on the side, taking the chance you might get caught and lose your primary partner; leave the relationship you're in to search for someone who does enjoy sex remembering they might be lacking in other areas your existing partner isn't); or make one last, desperate bid to get your partner to take your needs seriously. If you're at this point, I suspect you've tried many times to do this but give it one final go. Read chapter three, try counselling if you haven't already (see pages 183–185). Most of all, make sure your partner knows

how serious the problem is and how unhappy you will be if nothing changes. Stress that you're willing to try anything to get sex back on the agenda.

Most people at this point have gone without sex for an awfully long time, so it's fair to have this conversation. (If you're planning on delivering it three months after your wife's given birth to triplets, you're the one that needs a talking to!) If your partner refuses at this point, you're completely happy in every other way, and you think having no-strings sex on the side would satisfy you, then it's an understandable decision. I'm not justifying it – personally, if it got to that point, I'd leave and try to find someone more sexually compatible. But sometimes it can work. The person who doesn't want sex knows, though doesn't want confirmation, that their partner is getting it elsewhere. The sexually deprived person is satisfied and the primary relationship actually benefits. Of course, the not-so-happy ending could be you lose everything – your partner, family, house, dog, prized collection of Barbies – but if you couldn't survive without sex, you would have walked anyway.

05 Is no sex better than boring sex?

If you're both bored silly with sex, not having it for a while is OK – but only if it's done in a positive way. Simply looking at each other, shrugging your shoulders, and saying "Right, that's it for sex then!" will see you in the divorce courts (or popping up in someone *else's* bedroom) within a year. Do it deliberately and with purpose and it could be the best idea you've ever had.

American sex therapist Ian Kerner is all for abstinence – well, 30 days of it anyway. In his book, *The Sex Detox*, he lays out a 30-day plan designed to "reset, rewire, and ultimately rejuvenate" your love life. "Turn off the noise, take a necessary pause, and rebuild your love life from the inside out," he says. Ian's premise is that sometimes we get in so deep with our sex and relationship problems, the only way out is to start over again. Makes sense to me! It's pretty intensive emotionally because you delve through your past to work out what patterns of behaviour you're instinctively and systematically repeating (a bit like the erotic blueprints on page 26) but *well* worth making the effort. I'd highly recommend it (and Ian's other books!).

If you like the sound of time out from sex but don't fancy such a structured approach to it, ban any form of sex for two or three weeks to give yourselves a complete break. Then enforce a "no intercourse" ban for the month following. If you're forced to focus purely on foreplay – using just your tongue, hands, fingers, mouths – you're likely to be a damn sight more inventive than your usual rushed, obligatory fondle-and-feel on your way to the "main event". Banning anything makes it more appealing so by the time the month is over, you should both be gagging for penetrative sex. Indulge, then move straight into a "no oral sex" ban for the next month. After that, "no hands, just tongues" and so on. This not only keeps things interesting by introducing the "unavailable" element that makes sure-thing long-term sex so boring, it forces you to find new ways to orgasm so you're not just relying on one. The more different ways you can orgasm, the more you'll generally have.

Banning anything makes it more appealing. Bar bonking for a month and you'll both be gagging for intercourse once it's over!

Could an Affair Save Your Sex Life?

There's a theory that having sex on the side can keep married sex hot. And there's some truth to it. "Affair sex" can save your sex life – just not in the sense you think.

Can an affair save your sex life? "More like ruin my marriage, you nutter," I can hear you mutter. And, in most cases, you'd be quite right, of course. But an "affair" *can* save your sex life without destroying your marriage – just not how you might imagine. It's about capturing the sense of an affair, nicking the qualities that attract people to having them, and using them to turn married sex into affair sex. But I'm getting ahead of myself because this isn't just about that. What I want to do here is talk, in an honest and non-judgemental way, about the not-so-nice side of monogamy. The part when sex – even good sex – with your partner seems stale and unappealing. The part where sex – even very bad sex – with someone new seems unbearably exciting and beyond appealing. People react in various ways when this hits. Some constructive, some destructive. I think it's important you know what's going on out there because the more you've thought about how *you* would deal with it, the better you'll fare if it does happen to you.

You may or may not feel comfortable reading this. If you're tempted by, have had, or are having an affair, you'll read it with interest. If you're on the other side and have had your heart ripped out, still alive and beating, from your chest by a partner who had one or left you for someone else, you will hate it. NOT because – God forbid – I am in any way condoning affairs or suggesting one can save your marriage. (I am the daughter of a marriage broken by an affair.) But because it's tough reading. If this is you, I suggest you don't read it just now. This is a book about sex.

It doesn't deal with the emotional devastation caused by an affair, more the reasons why people have them. (I talk about the aftermath of an affair in my book *Hot Relationships* and there are many good books that can help you deal with this. Start with those first.)

The one point I can't resist touching on, however, is the whole "Should you confess to your partner?" dilemma. Actually, let's rephrase that to "Should you break your partner's heart, just to ease your own conscience?" No prizes for guessing which camp I'm in. Like most of the therapists I admire, I'm in the "don't confess, invest" camp. If you're having an affair or have had one, stop the affair, shut up, and invest in your relationship instead of someone else. That might just save it. There is one exception. If the affair is known or strongly suspected and your partner is bound to find out, you should speak up. A voluntary confession is then both sensible and pretty much mandatory.

Couples rarely choose to have an open relationship – probably because even if we're open to the idea of sex on the side, we don't want our partners to be. One rule for us, one for them.

Why we cling to monogamy

We've become a lot more flexible about relationships over the years. Mum, dad, and the kids isn't now the only model – just as acceptable are single parents, gay couples, couples who decide not to have kids, blended families, and combinations of all of the above. Divorce no longer has a stigma attached to it. But one thing hasn't budged at all – our insistence on monogamy. The rate of infidelity and affairs might be rising but we're still not moving away from the expectation that our partners sleep with us and only us. "We would rather kill a relationship than question its structure," says Esther Perel, a specialist on the topic.

Why do we cling so hard to something that clearly isn't working for a lot of people? Because everyone wants to feel special and *nothing* makes us feel more special than someone saying, "You are so wonderful, so beautiful, and so sexy, I will give up all others because you are enough." It's the ultimate compliment and when you're in the besotted early stage of love, monogamy seems not only entirely possible but positively appealing. Then you hit the five-year or 10-year mark and suddenly it's not quite so easy. Some people do manage to live up to their heartfelt pledge and live happily ever after, only ever kissing each

other's lips (not to mention other bits). But lots struggle. Sometimes it's both of you, sometimes it's one of you but pretty much all couples, even the most deeply in love, will freely admit monogamy isn't easy.

It's hard for one person to fulfil all our needs and while having an affair isn't thoughtful or respectful, the old theory that if you have an affair you don't love your partner, has pretty much been tossed out the window. Shirley Glass, a US fidelity specialist, found 56 per cent of men and 34 per cent of women who had affairs rated their marriage as happy or even very happy. Other experts also question the widespread belief that having an affair means there are serious problems in the relationship. Plenty of people who have a spouse and a lover are content in their primary relationships.

Flirting

But a lot of us don't give in to having an affair. How do these people cope? Well, most of us do it by flirting. Whether it's a sexy colleague, the handsome bartender, a girl who chats you up at a bar on that stag weekend, we're all prone to batting our eyelashes or flexing our pecs on the odd occasion. Luckily, most flirtations are pretty harmless. Jack Morin, author of *The Erotic Mind*, believes flirting can have a positive effect on relationships. "Seeing your partner get jealous isn't a

bad thing, feeling jealous isn't a bad thing. Knowing your partner gets hit on and still chooses you is a compliment. An injection of jealousy is the only thing capable of rescuing a relationship ruined by habit." In fact, one of the secrets to being sexually happy long term, he believes, lies in "inviting in the shadow of the third". The "third" is the person we've currently got our eye on/are fantasizing about. This means having the sort of relationship where you tell each other in a playful fashion about these flirtations. "When we are able to tell the truth safely, we are less inclined to keep secrets. It adds spice and reminds us that we don't own our partners. We see our partners through other people's eyes rather than the eyes of habit," Jack says. Obviously – *definitely* – have rules on how far it's to go, but I agree with him. If you're the sort of people who can cope with it, do it.

One-night stands

So flirting can be enough to satisfy the urge for novelty and attention. Or not. The next step and the most common breach of monogamy is a random one-night stand or one-night stands on an infrequent basis. These, believe me, are hard to resist. I was two years into a great relationship and madly in love – the thought of shagging anyone else was about as appealing as eating my own kidney. But I was travelling

home from New York and the plane got delayed. A few passengers waited in the bar (needless to say, I was one of them!) and I got chatting to a guy. Not hugely attractive but funny and sweet. We got told we were all being put up in a hotel. It seemed rude not to agree to have dinner when we'd been talking for three hours, so we did. More drinks, "wine goggles" working their magic, making him appear more and more attractive. Then the thought occurred to me, "I'll never see any of these people again. No one knows me. I could have sex with him and no one would ever know." Then he said, "I suppose we should go to bed," and the unspoken "Why not together?" hung there for a good minute or so. It would have been so goddamn easy.

I didn't go for it but believe me, I've had many fantasies about what would have happened if I had. And it wouldn't have been missionary with the lights off, it would have been naughty, dirty, and probably bloody marvellous, hanging-off-the-chandeliers sex. We're often more honest sexually with a stranger than the partner we love because we have nothing to lose. If the stranger curls their nose with disgust and pronounces us a "slut" or "pervert", who cares? If our partner did, the person we want to love and respect us, it would be the end of the world. And therein lies the problem of long-term sex and the reason why people have one-night stands when they're actually deeply in love with their partner.

The vast majority of one-off random "slip-ups" don't get found out. Some experts, Morin included, say that they're better off kept secret, "As long as strict safe sex guidelines are followed, dalliances typically pose no more threat to a relationship than masturbation, fantasizing about other people, or enjoying erotic videos or stories." Nothing is entirely risk free – you're still risking your relationship for an hour or two of pleasure – and neither Jack (nor I) advocate doing this. But this is a more common way of coping with the constraints of monogamy than you might think. Many consider having a one-night stand or even two days of decadence with a stranger under almost foolproof conditions (you're overseas, alone, your partner doesn't know what hotel you're staying in, you practise safe sex, there's no swapping of phone numbers, no real names – Facebook and My Space make everyone easy to find and therefore vulnerable) to be an acceptable risk. "It's realistic," says one man in what I know to be an incredibly happy marriage, "Not romantic but realistic." Some pragmatic couples actually spell this out at the start, acknowledging this might well happen on both sides but vowing always to protect each other by never letting it get found out.

Affairs

The next stage is an affair. And that's serious business. Why? Because it involves repeated visits to the same person – which often adds love as well as sex to the equation – and requires you to lie on a repeated basis. "I could cope with the affair, it's the fact she/he lied to my face for years that did me in" is a common reaction when betrayals come to light. Some develop into a secondary relationship that runs alongside the primary one. It rarely works when people leave their partner for their lover. People don't often leave and if they do, it doesn't work. You both know what you're capable of, so trust is low and once you put a hot lover in the role of loving spouse, the sexual spark fizzles fast. This is why people try their hardest to stay in what's essentially a "have your cake and eat it" position. Nothing more satisfying than enjoying the support and stability of your spouse and kids with an injection of excitement and naughty affair sex on the side.

Of course there's another way of dealing with the perceived drudgery of monogamy and that's having an open relationship. It's the least chosen option of all – probably because even if we're open to the idea of sex on the side, we don't want our partners to be. One rule for us, one for them. This is why most straight couples don't explore this option – though many gay guys do, quite successfully. They seem better able to separate sex into "sex for love" and "sex for fun". One version of this I have seen work is a couple I interviewed a few years back. "We'd both had affairs and our marriage was in trouble," the woman told me. "So we both sat down and I gave him permission to have the odd experience with a hooker when he's out of town. It seriously doesn't worry me. It's anonymous and he's not exactly going to have loving sex with her.

I'd so rather that than him have another affair! If he did have an affair, I'd divorce him." (The deal went both ways, even though she didn't act on it.)

Some relationship experts don't see "open relation-ships" as a bonkers idea. Perel says, "Couples who negotiate sexual boundaries are no less committed than those who don't. In fact, it's their desire to keep the relationship strong that leads them to explore other models of long-term love," she says. Granting your lover a "tourist visa" is one way of safeguarding the relationship against a far more threatening affair. Again, neither she (nor I) condone this method of dealing with temptation but we both encourage couples to view monogamy not as a given but a choice.

Affairs make my marriage work

"I have a great marriage and my husband is my best friend. But I don't find him sexually attractive – I don't think I ever did. So I have a guy I see two or three times a year. Having something exciting to look forward to is my incentive to get through the drudgery. Without the affair, it would be unbearable."

"We've been together nine years. It started off great but my career has really taken off and I want more than I did when I met my partner. It's awful because she knows I'm unhappy and want to leave but she has promised to do anything to keep us together. I can't leave because I can't break her heart and upset my daughter. I have affairs with girls I meet through my job to keep me sane. This is the only way I know to keep myself in the relationship. These affairs usually last around four months and are intense: I really fall for these women. The affair usually stops because they realize I won't leave my wife for them."

"I tried to get my husband interested in sex but it was always me making the effort so I gave up. I feel totally justified in having affairs. They are just about the sex and usually with married men who are in the same situation. I think my husband knows and turns a blind eye but I wouldn't put it to the test by confessing."

01

You're more likely to stray *if your parents, friends, or colleagues do or did. Their behaviour has effectively given you the thumbs up to do the same yourself.*

02

Every person you sleep with before marriage *increases your likelihood to cheat by one per cent. The "sow your wild oats" first theory is rubbish.*

03

Narcissists are ripe for affairs. *If you're focused on yourself and your own needs, you're more likely to indulge yourself and have a fling.*

04

If you think you're a better catch, *or better looking than your partner, you're more likely to cheat, feeling you "deserve it" for staying with them.*

Turn married sex into affair sex

Affairs are erotic because they're forbidden. This is why the minute people leave their partners for their lovers it goes horribly wrong. Affairs are sexually fragile. Give you both permission to sleep together and, as I said, the sexual charge has a tendency to disappear on that first trip to Ikea. Domesticity dampens desire pretty effectively. Affairs that turn into marriages are actually at a high risk of turning into low- or no-sex marriages. Ironic, when you initially risked your marriage, the dog, and that great little place you'd just finished doing up just to be able to get into each other's pants.

The other reason affairs are such a turn-on is that they share many of the elements sex had at the start. Adventure, newness, someone you haven't done 10,000 times. You anticipate and plan sexual encounters. And these are the strategies you can steal to recreate affair sex with your partner. Affairs teach you the value of anticipation and reflection: you grab sex when you can and it's not usually frequent so you spend most of the time either reliving the last time you had hot sex or imagining what the next will be like. Both things you can do as a settled monogamous couple. Affairs teach you to plan sexual encounters: you plan where to meet – whether it's going to be a seedy hotel or a posh, swanky one. You think about

what underwear he'll see when he peels off your clothes, what champagne you'll bring to dribble over her breasts. You think about what you can do to *really* impress. You plan, you think things through. Did you hear the words "plan" and "think things through"? It's not spontaneous sex, it's planned sex. Which is why it drives me *insane* when people screw their noses up when I tell them to plan sex. "Eww. How... forced. I'd never enjoy that," they sniff. Oh really? Affair sex is usually very hot sex and nearly all encounters are planned. So your point is? Shut up about the "sex should just happen" bollocks and start scheduling sex you can look forward to.

Affairs teach us to be playful. To give into desire and take what we want. Again, qualities that you can introduce to your relationship. Sex is fun! Give it priority and time. Let yourself fantasize about the stuff that *really* turns you on. Think of a way to indulge in it together so you can let loose those deep pit-of-the-tummy-please-let-me-have-it type desires. To have really good sex, you have to take risks – like revealing the sordid stuff you'd really like to do. A strong relationship will survive you sharing things that, to the two of you, seem a little daring. Start small: "Jane was talking about her new guy today, telling me how he puts his finger up her bottom while he's giving her oral. It made me feel quite turned on. Can you do that to me?" No risk, no growth. It's up to you how far you take it but at least try something to shake it up a bit.

What counts as cheating?

- **Full sex:** Have intercourse with someone else and you have well and truly cheated!

- **Oral sex:** Some men try to hide behind the Clinton excuse that unless there's penetration it doesn't count, but few people agree. It's cheating alright.

- **Kissing:** We're a bit "one rule for them, another for us" on this topic. In one study, 77 per cent of men and 89 per cent of women considered kissing cheating. But when it came to drunken snogs in nightclubs that "didn't mean anything", they were "harmless" when it was you doing the snogging. Not so if it's your partner – *that's* cheating!

- **"Emotional" affairs:** By this I mean seeing a "close friend" behind your partner's back but with no physical contact. Women consider this cheating, men don't. In reality, getting too close to a friend of the opposite sex is incredibly threatening to a relationship and often turns into an affair.

- **Net sex:** Sixty-six per cent of women in one study considered sexually explicit online chat as cheating. Eighty-three per cent of men disagreed – their motto was "unless it's physical it doesn't count". Hmmm. All well and good but it can quickly turn that way. And does in lots of cases.

- **Strip and lap-dancing clubs:** Again (are you sensing a theme here?) women consider this cheating, men don't. If it's the odd visit to a strip club with the boys, it's probably nothing to worry about. It's usually just a male bonding thing, eye candy, and a place that has a bar that stays open late when all the pubs are closed.

- **Porn:** Six per cent of women consider watching porn to be cheating. Not surprisingly, there wasn't a man to be found anywhere on the planet who agreed. Porn *can* be a huge problem if it's too regular or replacing sex with you but the odd dabble once or twice a week is normal and common.

Why people have affairs

Mira Kirshenbaum's *When Good People Have Affairs* is one of the few books that doesn't beat those having affairs around the head with a stick. If you're in one, buy it to help you decide what to do. She identifies 17 different types of affairs, some of which inspired my versions. Again, I'm not judging but I'm also by no means condoning any type of affair!

To revive your sex life: The affair's not about being madly besotted with someone else, it's done to wake up your partner sexually and romantically. They find out, they're upset, devastated… but suddenly they appreciate you, sex is hot again. *If this is you:* most of these affairs die a natural death and the marriage can actually get better. Unless the attempt to heat things up ends up causing a fire that destroys the lot.

To see if there's better out there: Comparison affairs are the most common female affair. You're doing it because certain emotional and sexual needs aren't being met. You compare your new lover to your husband to see if you're missing out. *If this is you:* you did this for a reason, now make a decision. If you're happier with the new person, leave. If you're not, finish it and put your energy back into your marriage.

To force you to leave: If you'd secretly be relieved if your partner found out, you're having an "exit affair". *If this is you:* leave. Don't pretend to yourself or your lover that you're leaving for them, you're not.

To keep the marriage: You're bored or sexually unfulfilled. You have no desire to leave but need the excitement of an affair. These are called "stabilizing" affairs or "three-legged stools": with two legs a stool would fall over, with three it's stable. *If this is you:* this actually works for lots of people but there's still a huge risk of being found out. Sometimes it's an unspoken agreement between couples.

You're having a mid-life crisis: Do I need to say more? *If this is you:* skip the affair and talk with a friend, your partner, or a counsellor about your fears of dreams slipping away, ageing, death – whatever it is you're preoccupied with. "Buy the sports car and skip the affair. It's a lot cheaper. On so many levels," says Mira. Couldn't put it better myself!

For revenge: It could be payback for an affair they had, or they're not paying you enough attention, etc. *If this is you:* if it's your only motive, you've achieved your aim. Stop it now – and don't even think about telling your partner, no matter how sweet the revenge.

To avoid facing the truth: You know you should leave or face your problems but instead you have a fling. *If this is you:* make a choice. You're hurting everyone more by staying in no-man's land.

To reward yourself: You've been a great husband/wife, mum/dad, you deserve it. Lots of people indulge this one by having a "safe" one-night encounter where the chances of getting found out are minimal. Trouble is, it turns into two nights, then three, then… *If this is you:* you've had your "treat", now stop it.

Your partner's not meeting a certain need: It might be sex you're lacking or maybe affection, or you might be feeling taken for granted. *If this is you:* once you get the need met by a lover, you'll know how important it is to you. If it wasn't crucial, stop the affair. If it was, leave.

To satisfy an experience your partner can't: *Desperate Housewives* provided the perfect example with Bree's husband having an affair with a S&M mistress. *If this is you:* sometimes doing it once gets it out the way. Other times, it reveals just how important it is. Are you sure your partner can't provide what you crave? If you intend leaving unless they do, you've got nothing to lose by asking.

To boost your ego: You want to see if you can still pull. *If this is you:* if you don't get found out and it's a relatively short affair, the confidence boost can actually renew the relationship. Risky way to do it though.

You want to trade up: The dutiful partner who helped you get there is shoved aside for a sparkly, young, pert model. *If this is you:* be aware that plenty of people miss the "old model" more than they expect.

In the "trade up" affair, the dutiful partner is rudely shoved aside for a sparkly, young, pert model. Don't be too hasty – most end up missing the "old model".

Nine Steps and Your Sex Life's Sorted

"Honey we need to talk" is a sentence guaranteed to strike fear in the heart of any half of a committed couple. Add "... about our sex life" on the end and we're practically having a coronary! But there is a way to talk through and solve sex problems stress-free – and you'll find it here.

Here's a sobering fact: many people would rather kiss goodbye to sex completely than talk about it with their partner. Another cheery little snippet: some people will go *years* being desperately unhappy or bored with sex without *ever* admitting it – even if their partner asks them outright if all is still OK. Now, if you're not as horrified as I am at this absolutely *ridiculous* state of affairs, then I really am going to bugger off to Brazil. (My manicurist is Brazilian and she told me everyone is sex obsessed and good-looking over there and that's why she left. Clearly I'm missing something.) If you suddenly hated your partner – rather than just hate having sex with them – would you speak up then? Most would. Going off sex seems somehow less surprising and... well, doesn't *everyone* go off sex eventually? Isn't that just what happens to couples long term?

So why bother addressing any problems? No point really. Forget the fact that you've faked it for five years. Or only do it on anniversaries. And both say "Who's got time for sex?" when you've polished off four novels each in the last month. The other reason people don't like talking about sex is that they worry it will make the problems worse not better. Let's address that one right now: the worst thing you can do is not talk about a sex problem. Leave it to fester away and the bitterness, resentment, apathy, indifference (add any and all negative emotions to the list depending on your particular angst) breeds away insidiously. Even if you don't care a hoot about your sex life, what about the marriage or relationship that's going to be the casualty?

Look, no one – and I mean no one – looks forward to discussing sex problems. Everyone gets all funny and a bit embarrassed because sex is so personal and private. If your partner says they don't like your technique, you feel hurt and like a bit of a twit really, and if your parts aren't working, you feel somehow ashamed and rejected. Thing is, though, if you're struggling and you don't have the dreaded "talk", your relationship won't survive and certainly won't grow. We all want our relationships to make us feel safe and protected from the big, bad world but if it's *always* comfortable, you're stuck.

When couples face problems and work through them, they feel insecure and anxious for a little while simply because they're both forced to change to fix the problem. It's not pleasant but if you appreciate it's all part of the process and don't panic, you come through the other side even stronger than before.

US therapist David Schnarch talks a lot about this in his book *Resurrecting Sex* and points out that try as you might to avoid the "anxious-growth" stage, the alternative is even worse. It would require you never trying anything new in bed (or out of it), sticking to the same old sex routines and techniques *for the rest of your life*. Now wouldn't that be fun? Not. If you did do this, you'd both end up so utterly bored and resentful, you'd feel... anxious. It's going to hit you anyway, so you might as well turn a positive spin and be in control of it! Anxiety is a sign your relationship is working not failing, says David. It's either going to force you to face problems or means you're facing them and working through stuff.

So how about it, guys? If you've got serious sex problems that need fixing, how about I take you through a pretty painless way of sorting them out? And even if you don't have any major worries, we all have something we're not entirely happy with sexually. How about you and your partner start getting some practice in now, so the little niggly thing doesn't turn into a big problem? There *is* a way to talk to your partner about sex and then still be talking to each other afterwards and this is it, in nine simple steps. So take a deep breath, and start at the beginning.

01 Think before you speak

Prepare for the chat: And I mean *really* prepare for it. Think about exactly what you want from this. What would be a brilliant result for you? Start there and work backwards. Focus on improving what's already there that is working and build on that rather than what's wrong or missing. Then when you speak to your partner, word what you want as a request, not a complaint. Say, "I miss the sex we used to have before the kids were born. Remember when (insert fond, sexy memory here)? How can we get back to that?" This is going to go down a hell of a lot better than, "We haven't had good sex since Jess was born. John said he wouldn't blame me if I got it elsewhere." Another example of why you should talk about things before you get really pissed off and say things you shouldn't.

> **David, married for 12 years, two kids**
> "It's all about listening and paying attention. I surprise my wife often – for her birthday, I kidnapped her from work and whisked her off to a hotel. I packed everything she needed without her knowing and laid out a designer dress I knew she liked in her size on the bed, along with roses in her favourite colour, chocolates, and champagne. It's not just about being romantic, I take a lot of mental notes as to what Maree likes and dislikes… and a lot of that just comes from listening."

Be aware of the 80/20 rule: Experts say issues that come up repeatedly and are hard to resolve are nearly always 80 per cent about the past and only 20 per cent about what's happening now. Be on full alert for this and don't be scared to get therapy to solve deep-seated problems that are interfering with your happiness.

Don't try to win: Most of us secretly think it's our partner's problem and they're the ones who have to change. But it's never one person's problem because nothing is black and white. Apart from violence, abuse, or addiction, all arguments are half your fault, half your partner's fault, says UK therapist Andrew Marshall. "I've yet to see a couple that don't share equal responsibility for their problems. Both sides have made equal if different contributions to it." *Both* of you need to be willing to change – and not just that, you both need to be willing to put the needs of the *relationship* above your own individual needs and desires. Yes, it's difficult but it can be done.

The absolute worst thing you can do is follow up a long, rambling, soul-baring, I've-never-told-anyone-this-before type rant with "Yes. But... " and launch straight into your side of the story.

potentially good lovers are pipped at the post simply because they've missed an important starter basic. Like him not making sure she's wet before trying that would-have-been-exquisite finger flutter on the clitoris. Or her using a softly-softly grip on a penis that's longing for a firm tug to get things started but would have loved it later on.

Re-learning something we believe we're quite good at is difficult – and, believe me, we all think we've got the basics mastered by 20. But even if it feels a bit like you're telling Mariah Carey she needs to go back to have singing lessons, plunge on. Before they launch (or don't launch) into the same old stuff, say "Hey... I just had an idea!" If you can make it sound like you just thought of it on the spot, get a gold star. Then say, "Instead of doing what we normally do (note the use of the word "normally" rather than "always" – "always" sounds accusing, "normal" sounds, well, normal), why don't we try this?" Then move yourself/their hand/penis/mouth/whatever to do what you'd prefer.

Most long-term lovers who aren't used to a partner making changes feel nervous when it happens, so follow this up with a reason why you want this change. Keep it simple, say "I've been reading that book we bought" or "There's a sex scene in the novel I'm reading and it gave me some ideas!" Or even "I was thinking about our sex life and think we're both so good at turning each other on (a lie but go with it) but

– we've stopped experimenting and thought we should try something new. (Turn to pages 148–65 for practical suggestions on ways to give techniques a makeover.)

04 Choose the right time

The right time to make changes: Attempt to change things, either actively (as in the previous point) or through discussion, when you're both feeling relaxed and happy, not tired and irritable. If you're nervous about the chat, it's natural to want to barge in and get it over as soon as possible rather than waiting for ideal conditions. But do wait. I promise you, catching your partner at the right moment is the key to this working.

The right place is usually *not* the bedroom: Technique problems can often be solved with hands-on solutions. But serious sex talks don't work in the bedroom because, for most couples, that's the scene of the crime. Instead, choose somewhere neutral where you both often chat and feel comfy. Sit facing each other, rather than side by side and maintain eye contact throughout. Body language is *crucial* to getting this right. Lean forwards, don't cross your arms or your legs, and pull your shoulders down. (They rise towards your ears when you're tense.) The more relaxed and open you look, the less threatened your partner will be. Keep your voice calm, use a warm tone, and speak clearly. If your voice starts to raise in pitch or you're shouting, it's time to stop. Watch for "micro-expressions": emotions that flit across our faces before we compose them. The slightest crinkle of your nose and your partner sees disgust. These expressions are hard to control but do your best.

05 Start the chat

Kick off by saying something nice – even if it kills you it can turn what would have been a frosty exchange into a real, honest discussion. Do it. Say, "I love you for doing this, I know you hate talking about stuff like this and it means a lot to me that you agreed",

Solve your sex problems – solo!

Is change possible if only one of you wants it? The answer is yes. In fact, if you want change you have the most control in the relationship – your partner doesn't have a choice but to change. Stop reacting to them in a certain way and they are forced to react differently to you. Satisfyingly sneaky, eh? Here's how to fix your sex life all by yourself:

- **No pressure, nagging, or ultimatums:** The more you ask someone to do something they don't want to, the more they'll resist it. Getting angry is also pointless. The person who's up for change is usually better educated, more confident, and has higher self-esteem than the person who's not. It takes courage to admit there's a problem and try to fix it. You're brave, they're scared. Feel sorry for them if you like but don't feel angry. On the other hand, don't expect *them* to see it this way or congratulate you for making an effort! You won't be popular for making them feel uneasy (though you will later, when you're having fantastic sex again!)

- **Stop pushing information:** So you've devoured tons of books and checked out every internet site on the topic. Great! Suggest your partner reads any particularly helpful stuff but if they don't want to, don't sulk. Instead, ask them if you can tell them about it. Some people don't like reading or are so slow, by the time they've read their daily horoscope it's a day out of date. Deliver the information the way they want it.

- **Dangle the rewards rather than point out the dangers:** US therapist Jack Morin says we have two main motivations to change: pushes and pulls. Pushes are things that force you into action when your situation becomes dire (your sex life is so boring, the cat doesn't even move off the bed). Pulls are motivators that promise the benefits of change (the possibility of shagging in the shower again). Most of us respond far better to pulls than pushes, so encourage your partner by dangling rewards.

even if you are secretly thinking, "This is the sodding fourth time I've tried to pin you down about this, asshole." Or, "Honey, I know we're going through a rough time but I love you, we're so going to sort it out."

No finger-pointing: Only do any of the following if you want to end the chat with a screaming row: call each other names ("You're such a selfish bastard" instantly springs to mind, not sure why), blame or finger-point instead of "When you do such-and-such, it ruins the moment for me" say "I really like it when you do such-and-such"), hurl off a sexual insult ("Your willy's so small, I'm surprised I can feel it!"), make comparisons to previous partners ("Carla used to orgasm in three minutes"), complain about your sex life to mutual friends (this is a gross betrayal and the version that makes its way back is usually distorted and overexaggerated).

06 Stay in the moment

Really listen: Don't spend the time when they're talking to work out your response. Your job is to thoroughly understand what your partner is saying, that's it. Period. Ask questions but don't interrupt and only ask questions designed to bring out more of what's inside your partner. And even if you can see the final episode of your favourite TV show starting in the living room, don't get distracted.

Give each other time to express thoughts: One of the most common complaints I get from boyfriends is that I speak for them. Three words in, I guess what's coming and jump in to finish their sentences. Even more galling, apparently, is that I'm right most of the time. (Ha!) Sadly, while I think I'm helping to clarify their thoughts, they just see it as me putting words in their mouth and "rushing" them. Learn from my mistake. People feel heard when there's nothing left for them to say. So let them rattle on and on and on, even if you got the point 20 minutes ago. Also resist the urge to give your opinion early on – this isn't about you even if it is about you! It's about their feelings about you! Be patient and give them the same attention you want back when it's your turn. Don't expect them to listen if you don't.

Issues that come up time and time again and are hard to resolve are nearly always 80 per cent about the past and only 20 per cent about what's happening now.

07 Make them feel heard

Reward their efforts: When they've (finally) trickled off into silence, repeat back what you've understood. "So what you're saying is…" The absolute *worst* thing you can do is follow up a long, rambling, soul-baring, I've-never-told-anyone-this-before type rant with "Yes. But…" and launch straight into your side of the story. That one word "Yes" does not match the effort they've put in. Let them know *you* know how hard it was talking about things that are intensely personal and vulnerable.

Check, check, and check again: Get into the habit of saying "Is this what you mean?" or "Let me repeat back what I think you just said" whenever your partner's talking about something important. Say "Is that clear?" and "Did you understand what I said then?"

08 Don't be derailed

Don't give too much detail: Sorry to be sexist but I'm talking to us girlies here. We're generally the ones who embellish to the point where the poor guy's lost after the first five minutes, trying desperately to work out which bit he was supposed to pay attention to. Like, "You remember last Wednesday when your Aunt Doris was here for dinner and I burnt the potatoes and she stayed way too late? Well, I know by the time we both got to bed after putting the kids down it was really late but I still felt like we, umm, I don't know, I think we started having intercourse before I was really ready." Leave Aunt Doris out of it and just say, "I'd like more foreplay." Guys tend to go to the other extreme, giving too *little* detail which also isn't terribly helpful. A good rule for both is to start by stating what you want, clearly and directly, then provide or ask for further explanation if you need it.

Stick to one issue at a time: Unless something gets said that totally eclipses what you're trying to solve ("Actually the reason I'm not having sex with you is because I'm gay"), don't be derailed. If your partner says "Well, what about the time when you did such-and-such?" refuse to be drawn into it. Stay calm and say "You're clearly still upset about that, so let's talk about it next time. But I think it's really important we stay on this topic for this chat." A lot of arguments don't get solved and run in frustrating circles because couples segue into different directions in an attempt to one-up their partner.

09 Know when to stop

Don't talk for too long: Having said give each other time, you also need to know when to stop. You're better off having a few smaller chats than thrashing stuff around for hours… and hours. Aim for between half and one hour. If it's going really well and you both feel close to a breakthrough, keep going. Otherwise, it's perfectly OK to stop and pick it up again later.

Do what you said you'd do: You'd be amazed how many couples manage to execute the perfect sex talk but then fall at the last hurdle because they don't actually action the solution they came up with. Don't wait for your partner to stick to their side of the "bargain", stick to yours. Now. Don't wait for them to do it, be the first.

> **Anna, 42, divorced**
> **"I left my previous partner because he refused to discuss anything. Whenever I'd say I wasn't happy about something, his answer was 'Don't be ridiculous, it's fine.' When I met my new boyfriend, I said 'If I can't talk to you, forget it.' Happily, he'll cheerfully talk about anything and the difference is extraordinary."**

What I've learnt so far...

To turn myself on, rather than expect my partner to do it. I'll make myself feel like sex, rather than wait for it to happen.

To be generous with sex and make sure I'm good at it. Enthusiasm counts but good technique is crucial long term.

To have naughty affair sex as often as possible – so long as it's my partner I'm having it with.

To talk about and solve sex problems as they happen, rather than let niggly little things turn into big bedroom monsters.

To choose my battles wisely and focus on all that's good in my sex life, as well as fix what's not.

To stop trying to win because it's never just one person's fault. I also vow to put the relationship needs above my own.

5
How to
Have
Just-Met
Sex

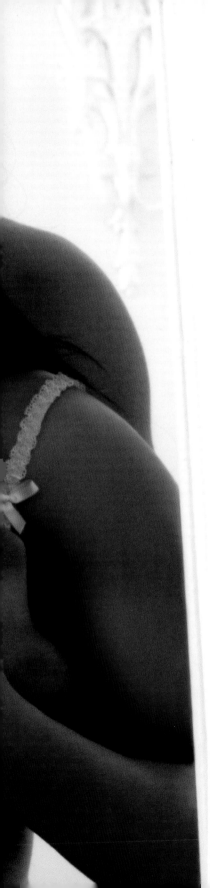

Sex
Makeovers
to Change
Your Life

Guilty of using the same tired, old techniques time and time again? Take a crash masterclass in oral, hand-jobs, and anal play, perk up your positions, and check out the new designer sex toys that you'll flaunt, not hide.

If you've worked through this book in a fairly logical order (started at the beginning and only flipped ahead to check out the gorgeous bods on display), you should by now have a pretty clear idea of what needs work in your sex life and relationship. You'll also (hopefully!) have an action plan sorted from the various solutions I've presented. In this chapter, we're going to get down to the nitty-gritty of sex by going back to the basics and focusing on technique. Not just because it's the fun part but because lots of people – perhaps you or your partner included – form bad habits very early on that never, ever get rectified. I want you to check you're not guilty of committing any classic mistakes and I'm going to suggest a few new things for you to try.

Now, because we'd all love to think long-standing sex problems can be solved by a killer twirl of the tongue or a brilliantly cunning hand-job manoeuvre, there's a temptation to skip straight to this practical part of the book and bypass the earlier, higher-effort talky, emotional bits. If you've done just that and you don't have any sex problems, great! Everyone else, *cannot* collect £200 and pass Go. Back to the beginning for you boys and girls, because while good technique is certainly a big factor for long-term sexual satisfaction, it'll do diddly-squat if you're wrestling with other stuff. So, if we're all – literally – on the right page, let's start. Here, I've pulled together what I think are crucial dos and don'ts and creamed off my favourite "fancy" moves and tips.

Makeover your... mouths

For her

Brush up on the basics

- **You need access to his testicles, anus, and perineum** as well as being able to grasp the base of the penis and slide the other hand up and over. In other words, you need *room*. Also make sure you're not at an angle where your hand is going to end up in a weird position and get twisted or cramped.
- **It's all about height.** Use stairs, pillows, or items of furniture to align his bits with your mouth.
- **Use your hand as well as your mouth.** It avoids that dreadfully embarrassing bobbing-for-apples moment when you first put him in your mouth. Slide your hand up and down with your mouth following in hot pursuit.
- **Create good suction** but don't suck. (I know, schoolgirl error, but just in case you've been locked in a nunnery for the past 10 years.)
- **Relax the muscles in your jaw and neck** and push your lips *out* rather than pull them in so that they cover your teeth.
- **Start slowly and gently,** work up to fast and firm, and keep a consistent rhythm.
- **Concentrate stimulation on the head of the penis,** the most sensitive part, but do take all of him in your mouth now and then for porn appeal.

Check you're not guilty of...

- **Leaving him flapping about at the crucial moment.** If you don't want to swallow, just remove your mouth, keep working with your hand, and let him ejaculate somewhere nice (like all over your breasts, maybe).

- **Being squeamish.** If you're worried about smell or taste, have a shower together first and give it a good old wash. Do it sexily and he'll think it's all part of foreplay.
- **Looking like you'd rather be anywhere else but doing what you're doing.** There is such a thing as a bad BJ: one that's delivered with zero enthusiasm or barely disguised disgust.

Now try...

A new position

- **He kneels over you** while you lie on your back, head on the pillows. He supports his weight on the wall behind the bed with his hands.
- **He sits on the side of the bed** while you kneel before him.
- **He leans against a wall,** you kneel in front of him.
- **You sit on the side of the bed** while he stands in front of you. (My fave!)

A new technique

- **Lick it like it's a lollipop.** Hold him at the base, then make broad, long, showy licks on the shaft. The slower you lick from the base to the head, the bigger he'll think he is.
- **Twist it.** Make a fist around the base and move it up and down as you usually do, except this time twist your hand when you reach the head and follow it with a swirl of your tongue.
- **Hold your hand in an L-shape on its side** and position it between his legs, then push up firmly. This provides strong pressure on the perineum and base of his testicles, and it's especially effective as he's about to orgasm.
- **Put your hand on his lower belly** and rub slowly but firmly to stimulate his inner penis.

For him

Brush up on the basics

- **Make sure you're comfortable.** Put pillows under your forearms if you're in the traditional position and slip a pillow underneath her bottom to make access easier. Make sure your neck isn't at a weird angle so you can settle in, keep and your tongue and jaw relaxed so you can last longer.

- **Keep it wet** – lots of saliva and a glass of water by the bed in case your mouth dries up.
- **Keep it slow, gentle, and consistent:** your mantra for giving oral sex that ends in a real orgasm rather than a "poor bastard's been down there for ages" fake one.
- **Use your hands as well as your tongue.** It's not cheating to wait until she's really aroused, then slide one or two fingers up and down between the inner lips as you continue to lick her. Some women like it if you insert one or two fingers inside, others find it detracts from the main event – your tongue.

Check you're not guilty of...

- **Using the tip of a stiff tongue** rather than the flat of it. First up, your tongue will be knackered out in about five minutes. Second, it feels too hard on her end (especially at the start). Third, if you flatten out your tongue as much as possible, it covers a bigger area and feels deliciously soft and squishy. Wiggle it around a little and she's nearly there.
- **Expecting an orgasm in five minutes.** Unless she's massively turned on, settle in for the long haul. Around 20 minutes is about right. Yes, really.

Now try...

Some new moves

- **Place a flat, wide, relaxed tongue over the whole clitoral area** and gently swish from side to side. Then alternate with fast, darting licks with a tenser tongue. (I'm not contradicting myself, I said "tenser" not tense.)
- **Pull up the fleshy part of her mons to expose her clitoris,** then make slow circles with a relaxed tongue around the rim. Circle one way, then reverse it.

- **Get her to make a "V" with her fingers,** positioning them where she wants you to focus, then lick between them. The turn-on isn't just her knowing you'll be dead on target for where she likes being licked most; there's something deliciously naughty about having her fingers and bits licked at the same time.
- **Spell out the letters of the alphabet with your tongue** as you're licking her clitoris. An oldie but still one of the simplest, most effective techniques around. It ensures you're constantly stimulating a new area, heightens sensation, and ensures she doesn't get oversensitive.
- **Imagine a clock dial is surrounding the vaginal area.** Twelve o'clock is at the top end where the clitoris is, six o'clock is down near her bottom. She can then use the clock as an instructional device. Saying "two o'clock" is a hell of a lot easier than doing the endless, "Left, no not that far, a bit to the right, now up a bit…" malarkey.
- **If your tongue gets tired,** move your head from side to side and up and down instead or simply hold it still against her and let her wiggle against you.

New position, new sensation

- **She puts her legs over your shoulders** or pulls them up to her chest while lying on her back.
- **She's on all fours, you slide underneath** (facing in the opposite direction to her) and use pillows to bring you up to the right height or – even better – you lick her from behind (facing the same way).
- **She's on her side,** you're between her thighs so her top leg is around your neck.
- **She sits on the side of the bed,** lies back, then puts her feet or knees on your shoulders.
- **You lie back on the bed, she straddles you,** lowering her genitals onto your face.
- **She stands with her legs apart,** leaning back against a wall.

The turn-on isn't just her knowing you'll be dead on target for where she likes being licked most, there's something deliciously naughty about having her fingers and bits licked at the same time. Keep your tongue flat and deliciously soft and squishy, and simply wiggle it.

Makeover your... hands

For her

Brush up on the basics

- **Choose your position depending on whether you're right- or left-handed.** One side's going to feel *way* more comfy and easier than the other.
- **Make sure you have room to move,** are easily able to use both hands, and he's at the right height to manipulate easily. This means the lazy-girl option of "I'll just lie beside him on the bed" is out.
- **Get him to show you how he masturbates** and copy it as closely as you can. Men give themselves a *lot* of hand-jobs (you seriously don't have a clue just how many!) and he's got it down to a fine art. Pay *particular* attention to *exactly* where he places his hand/fingers at the start. Imitate how he holds his hand – he'll usually make a loose fist or he'll put all his fingers on one side and thumb on the other – then start your hand-job exactly where he started his. Watch whether he works right up and over the shaft or just to the rim of the head.
- **You have two hands, use them.** If they're not both working on his penis, one should be fondling his testicles, pressing on the perineum, indulging in some anal play, tweaking his nipples…
- **Watch your grip.** As a basic rule of thumb: the harder you hold, the slower the stroke. When you loosen your grip, speed up the strokes.
- **Aim for one, smooth action** rather than a series of jerky movements. If you're going to switch between techniques, try to make the transition seamless.
- **Get him to put his hand on top of yours** once you get going to check you're spot on. He can then adjust the pressure and pace to pretty much perfect!

The size of his penis dictates the pressure: use a lighter touch for smaller penises and a good, firm hand for the big boys.

Now try...

A new position
- **Stand behind him** and reach your hands around.
- **He stands, you sit on the bed** in front of him or both sit on the side of the bed, you stay upright, he gets to lie back.
- **Straddle him** and sit lightly on his tummy, facing his feet.

A new technique
- **Slide upwards till you reach the head then pause,** rub your palm over the head in a small circle, then let your hand drop down the other side of the penis until you're back at base camp but on the opposite side with your hand facing the opposite way. Then reverse.
- **Alternate 10 slow strokes with a quick, firm pump** up and down. Add an extra pump as you keep going.
- **Roll his penis between two flat palms** as though it's pastry.
- **Make two rings around his penis with the thumb and index finger of each hand.** Place them next to each other in the middle of the shaft then continually slide in opposite directions simultaneously.
- **Wear a strand of beads to bed,** then take them off, slide them through your hands (sneakily checking there are no rough edges), wrap them around your hand or the shaft of his penis and slide up and down.
- **Slide a well-lubed finger inside his anus** as you continue to work on him.
- **Slide a male masturbation sleeve** (see page 162) over him, hold the base and move it up and down.

Her hand-job no-nos

- **Not customizing.** The size of his penis dictates the pressure you should use. Generally, use a lighter touch for smaller penises and a good, firm hand for the big boys.
- **Not using lube.** Saliva is OK, using the little bit of pre-ejaculatory fluid some men leak early on is better but best for a hand-job is always a dollop of lube. Not so much that there's no friction but enough so it's a nice, slippery ride.

For him

Brush up on the basics
- **Add some lube,** unless she's very, very wet, and touch her more slowly and more gently than you think. "Too rough" is the most common complaint.
- **Keep your strokes light, consistent, and continuous.** Yes, you are sensing a theme here…
- **Don't show off by constantly changing techniques.** You won't score brownie points but big, ugly black marks – especially if she's on the verge of climaxing. Try one or two (max. three) techniques at the start and settle on which she says feels best.
- **Be inventive** but not offended if she constantly wants the same old thing. Lots of women have one particular stroke that does it for them. The only changes she may want you to make are to speed it up and use more pressure as she nears orgasm.
- **Follow her lead.** If she lifts towards your hand, she wants a firmer touch. If she pulls away, go softer. If you get a sharp "*Owww!*" and a filthy look, you're the cliché and just plain rough. Go to the bottom of the class.

Abby, 34, married four years
"**Once you've been together for a while, that frantic lust slowly ebbs away and that's the stage that separates the good lovers from the bad. That's when you notice sexual technique – good or bad. My husband gives the best hand jobs I have ever had – and I've had my fair share! Everything is exactly as I love it. Married four years and just thinking about him doing it is still enough to get me hot.**"

- **Use the flat of your finger** and the whole pad of your fingertip to rub or slide, rather than just the tip. It feels softer and covers a much larger area.

Sins punishable by death
- **Stopping if she goes suddenly quiet, still, and tense.** She hasn't just heard someone downstairs, she's having an orgasm. Forget the thrashing "Yes, yes, *yesssssssss!!!!*" you see in films, this is what lots of women do when they climax.
- **Thinking a hand-job is purely about thrusting your fingers inside her like a pretend penis.** Not to say it doesn't feel nice if you slip in and out occasionally (note the word "occasionally"), just don't forget to go back to the undisputed star of the orgasm show, the clitoris.
- **Thinking one technique suits all.** It doesn't. The hand-job should be as individual as she is.

Now try...

A new position
- **Get her to sit with her legs spread,** then sit behind her, your legs on either side of hers. Then use both hands on her clitoris or one on her breasts, the other down below.
- **Sit in a chair** and get her to sit on your lap.

A new technique
- **Slide your middle finger gently between her inner lips,** then rock it from side to side.
- **Cross your middle finger over your index finger and slide them in and out of her,** twisting like a screw. No, I'm not contradicting myself because you're using the fingers of your other hand to simultaneously circle her clitoris. Penetration plus clitoral stimulation is a dynamic combo!
- **Change direction when you circle,** moving first one way, then the other. Zig-zag, move up and down, and pay particular attention to which side elicits the biggest moans. Lots of women are more sensitive on one side.
- **Insert a few fingers inside her,** curving them up to the "tummy side" of her vagina, with your other hand push down on her lower abdomen.

Makeover your... positions

For her

Classic female foibles

- **Lying back and letting him do everything.** Share the load and if you can't do that, at least even it with enthusiasm. Thrust your hips up to meet his, squeeze your pelvic muscles tight every time he thrusts, grab his buttocks, and put your hands flat behind you on the wall behind the bed to give leverage.
- **Skipping your Kegels.** Yes alright already, I know I do bang on about this one. But squeezing and holding your pelvic floor muscles on a regular basis doesn't just make intercourse feel better his end, it'll feel better yours as well. The more toned you are, the easier you'll orgasm and the better it will feel.
- **Stressing if he loses his erection.** It's not a wind-up toy, you know! It's normal for him to go hard, soft, hard, semi-soft, sort of hard, soft, really hard in the one session. It's no reflection on anything, so park the paranoia.

Things to do more of...

- **Use your legs during missionary.** If you want him deeper, push your knees into his armpits or straighten your legs and hold them high into the air, leaning them back towards your head, as though you're trying to touch your toes on the wall behind (looks showy and athletic but is actually dead easy!). Up the friction by letting him penetrate first, then hold your legs straight and together with his legs *outside* yours.
- **Arch during rear entry.** Arch your back to pull him deeper inside you, push your chest to the floor, and spread your legs wider. If you want him shallower,

flatten your back and keep your hips tucked under. Use your arms to alter the angle of penetration: hold yourself up on your hands or rest your chest on the bed and lay your arms flat out in front of you.

- **Show off on top.** Spread yourself wide open with your hand so that you can both watch him disappear inside you. Or sit him in a chair (without arms) and lap-dance: knead your breasts, play with your clitoris, and tease by letting him penetrate a little before lifting yourself off… then on again. Move to an armchair, let him lie back, jump on top again, then lean back so your hands are on his knees and your legs on the top of the back of the chair. Says American sexpert Sadie Allison, "What *can't* he see in this position? It's the ultimate *eye-candy treat!*"

For him

His top penetration sins

- **A bad thrusting style.** Hammering away like a jackhammer is still up there on the female "Pet Male Hates" list. I'm constantly amazed at the amount of guys out there who seem to think this is the only way to "do it"! It's the guys who swivel their hips and move in sexy circles rather than just thrust in and out who we boast about to our girlfriends. Yes, it really is that *easy* – now go practise!
- **Rushing penetration.** A few pathetic fumbles to check if she's wet do not make her ready for you to plunge on in. Unless you're both fired up for a quickie, keep that penis away until you've paid some lip service and at least inserted some fingers to check she's lubricated and ready for you.
- **Taking too long.** Yes there are exceptions and times when you both want a session to last six weeks but, as a rule, intercourse that lasts longer than 20 minutes has most women yawning rather than groaning.
- **Constantly changing positions.** A favourite of men who fancy themselves as "studs" in the bedroom. You think it's impressive chucking her this way and that, she just thinks "Tedious try-hard". And deletes your number the second you're out the door. If you want to change position, move seamlessly to a similar pose such as side-by-side to rear-entry.

Revamp your thrusting

- **Make her beg for it.** Hold your penis and rub the baby-soft head over her clitoris and vulva. Then wait until she's *begging* for you to "do her", before penetrating. (If she doesn't beg, you're doing the job a little *too* well. Never mind though… keep going until she climaxes, then penetrate immediately after to ride the final waves of her orgasm.)
- **Try one gloriously slow, deep plunge,** then pull right back for four shallower pumps before doing another deep thrust. Keep repeating.
- **Grab her buttocks** to pull her pelvis close, position your pubic bone so it's pressing against her clitoris, and grind in relentlessly slow circles.
- **Angle your penis different ways** in each position to target different areas of her vaginal wall. The most sensitive side is usually the bit under her tummy.
- **It's fine to let go and thrust hard and fast,** just don't do it for ages – and be aware of the consequences. (Her being knocked unconscious by you bashing her head against the wall, for instance.)
- **Pull her close,** then tip your pelvis up and down and from side to side.
- **Thrust somewhere other than the obvious.** Get her to hold her breasts together or try between her *closed* thighs. It's a gentle, non-invasive way to have sex if she doesn't want to or doesn't like doing it during her period.

- **Expecting to come together.** Where have you been for the last 10 years? First up, only 20 per cent of women actually orgasm during penetration (unless you add some extras like clitoral stimulation). Secondly, the chances of it coinciding with yours are low, not the norm. Don't make her fake it like all your previous partners – instead give her an orgasm first, then enjoy yours guilt-free.
- **Getting really drunk.** If you can actually manage an erection, it will be soft like a pillow rather than hard like a rock and you'll be so desensitized, it'll take you six years to orgasm. If she's drunk too, go for it. If you've been out with the boys and she's already tucked up in bed, do both of you a favour and snore in the spare room.

For both of you

Suit the mood

- **You're having a fat day.** Rear entry is the most flattering if it's her (lucky guess). Push your bottom high to make your waist look tiny and thighs super-slim. Lean forward onto a pile of pillows to hide your tummy.
- **You're sleepy.** She lies on her side, her back to his front. She lifts her bottom to allow him to penetrate, then tightens her thighs for maximum friction.
- **You're drunk.** Either rip your clothes off in the hallway, leaning heavily against the wall, or opt for missionary. You're both lying down (handy when you can't stand up) and with him on top, gravity works in favour of a penis prone to "brewer's droop". If his erection fails, use your tongues instead.
- **You've got your period.** The shower is an obvious choice for the built-in clean-up! She puts her hands on the shower wall and stands on tip-toes, he enters from behind as she pushes her bottom up and out.

Transform any position

- **Add pillows.** They make any position feel better, more comfortable – and more doable. Drape rugs over furniture to cover pointy corners or on the floor to save you from scratchy carpet.
- **Turn around.** Face in the same direction if you're side-by-side or she's on top.
- **Move her legs** to alter the angle of her vagina, creating a tighter fit and deeper penetration.
- **Add a vibrator** so neither of you ends up with hand cramps trying to play with her clitoris.
- **Do it when you usually don't.** An unplanned spontaneous quickie wins hands down because it reminds us of sex at the oh-so-easy start.
- **Do it somewhere new.** On the sofa, in a recliner, in the cellar or attic for secret, scary kicks, on the stairs, in seedy motels, as posh a hotel as you can afford, on a boat, in a swimming pool, under the blanket on a plane, in a tent, in a chauffeur-driven car. And then start getting creative…

Naughty it up…

Say filthy things Grab buttocks and biceps Nip necks and thighs Suck their toes Switch to oral and back Cradle his testicles Add a penis ring Watch his penis disappear Pull her hair Watch in a mirror Spank her Knead her breasts Add anal play

Some people find the thought of "rimming" outrageously sexy while others would rather cut the fingers off with a saw, one by one

01

Finger play is the logical place to start. Lightly rub around the outside and work up to inserting a finger.

02

Spanking is a great option if neither of you are really into being penetrated with fingers, tongues, penises...

03

Rimming involves licking the outside of the anus. Some people like a tongue inserted, others not so much.

04

Anal intercourse has skipped over from being "taboo" to something lots of couples now enjoy.

Makeover your... bottoms

Why you should try anal play

- **Everyone else is.** Thirty-seven per cent of men and 35 per cent of women report trying anal intercourse at least once. Of those, around half continue to do it regularly.
- **It's a hot spot for both sexes.** The anus is packed with nerve endings – particularly for men because it's the home of the prostate gland (better known as the male G-spot).
- **There are four simple rules.** Start slow (as in the time between trying a finger and trying a penis is weeks, rather than the same session). Be gentle. Stop if it feels too painful. And don't suggest it if your partner's just polished off a three-course gassy dinner, especially one containing brussel sprouts. Or chick peas. Or possibly broccoli. Many a lover's hand has been brushed aside while tentatively exploring, never to return again, not because their partner

wasn't interested but because they were worried... well, you work it out. They were simply too embarrassed to admit why they weren't so keen, you feel rejected and a bit silly because your "move" got rejected... it can so easily happen.

At least give this a whirl...

- **Insert a finger.** This is how most people start experimenting with anal play. It's safe but saucy, not too out-there but naughty enough to get the heart pumping, doesn't hurt, and feels *amazing* because there are highly sensitive nerve endings inside the rectum of both sexes. Simply apply some lube to your finger or your partner's bottom and start by rubbing your fingertip gently around the rim of the anus until the muscles relax. Use the finger you point with to begin with, inserting it a tiny way, then waiting for the rectum to get used to this new, if welcome, intruder. Keep inserting a little at a time and once it's all in there, either make a "come here" stroking motion or make little circles. Do NOT use a fierce, in-out thrusting motion, like he does inside the vagina, unless you're asked to – and especially not the first time.
- **Try a butt plug.** They're usually made of rubber, silicone, or jelly and shaped like little penises that have eaten too much – they expand in the middle – with a flared end (to stop it disappearing up you-know-where). Even if you're not in the slightest bit interested in ever taking anal stimulation further than

just a finger or a small toy like this one, the butt plug is a non-threatening way to explore and experience the highly arousing sensations produced by anal stimulation. Use the same steps as for a finger (see previous point) to insert it, then simply leave it there during oral sex or intercourse to add an erotic edge. They make you feel pleasantly "filled up", provide pleasant pressure on everything else (the rectum shares a wall with the vagina) – and they get your bottom used to relaxing around an inserted object (just in case you change your mind about the other). You can buy vibrating butt plugs or insert a slim vibrator a little way to see if you like the sensation (without letting go, unless it has a flared end).

- **Spank their bottom.** Bend them over your knee or do it during sex when you've got good access. Wait until they're fully aroused (the more turned on we are, the more receptive we are to erotic "pain"), then run your hand lightly over those yummy, fleshy orbs, simply enjoying the feel of them. Now cup your hand slightly, keep your fingers together, and administer a light spank in a slightly upward motion. Your first

spank will sound more dramatic than it feels but if they aren't expecting it, they'll be shocked. Immediately massage the area for a few seconds, laugh, or fix them with a wicked look (depending on which you think will convince them to let you continue), then try another spank, no later than 3–5 seconds apart. Cover both cheeks, aiming for the lower (fleshier) part. If they like it, increase the force a little. If you both enjoy it, splash out on soft whips or riding crops (see page 164).

Go on, be brave

- **Try rimming,** licking the "rim" of the anus and/ or inserting a stiff tongue inside it. As you can imagine, some people find the thought outrageously sexy while others would rather cut their fingers off with a saw, one by one. If it appeals but you're squeamish, cover the opening with a piece of cling film. (It stops infection as well.)
- **Attempt anal intercourse** – you can always stop if you hate it! Now, if you've skipped all the other stuff

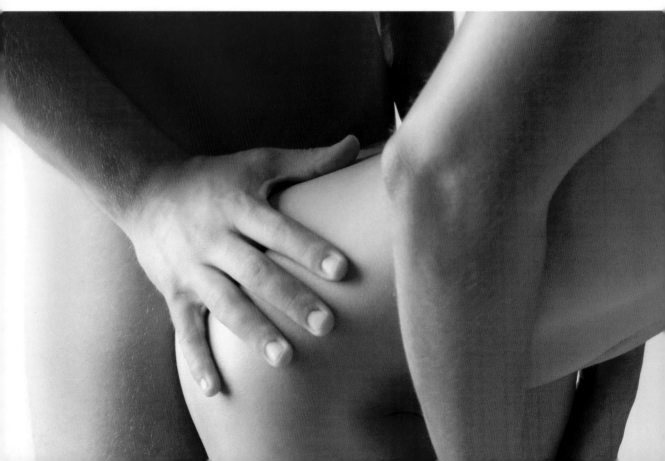

and come straight to this bit, pay attention: you should never go straight into anal intercourse without having tried other stuff first (fingers, dildos, butt plugs, etc). If you have, here's what to do. (I've written it from the perspective of the person penetrating, by the way, and this is a crash course. There are more detailed guides in my books *superhotsex* and *Sextasy*.) Apply lots of lube to both your penis and her bottom, then rub the penis head against the opening. Wait for her anus to relax and open and let her back onto your penis, rather than you do the penetrating. Hold your penis at the base and wait until the head (only) penetrates. Pause until she says it's OK to go further and insert a little at a time, *very* slowly. Once it's all in, pause again, then do slow, gentle, shallow thrusts. Angle yourself so you're aiming for her belly button. Stop regularly to apply more lubrication and exit as slowly as you entered – go too fast, and the muscles will tense and spasm. As I always say, anal sex is the one type of sex you really can do "wrong"! If you've never tried it before, educate yourself properly first.

Robert, 46, living with partner
"Anal sex is something men always want to try and women try to avoid because they think it will hurt like hell! And it does if you rush it. I tried it once in my youth and the girl told me to stop after I'd got about an inch in. It was a total disaster but since then I've tried it a couple of times, taking it slowly and doing everything the books say to do, and it was brilliant. She enjoyed it as much as I did."

Makeover your... toy chest

Invest in some sex toys

- **Because all of a sudden they're classy.** Sex toys are out and proud with designer pedigrees, nestling next to iPhones in Prada handbags as something to flaunt rather than smuggle in with your smalls. Kate Moss has a gold-plated Jimmyjane vibe (£226) but if that's too low rent, you could fork out £2,500 for the same design in platinum with diamonds. Class doesn't necessarily mean expensive – there's tons of fun, sexy, affordable stuff out there! Personally, I think it's because a lot of sex toys are now being designed by women, taking them away from the old-school ghastly flesh-coloured, veiny pretend penises to toys so pretty, you want to show them off. See page 191 for where to look for great sex toys.
- **There are lots for couples.** In the past, sex toys were something you bought and used solo. We kept them stuffed deep in our knicker drawer, surreptitiously hidden from prying eyes. Today, sales of "couple" toys are on the increase, with any self-respecting couple boasting at least one or three. Not only are there more to choose from – bondage kits, sex "furniture", lubricants that tingle your bits – toys that used to be used alone, like vibrators and male masturbators, are now used together. Being able to shop online on classy websites has also revolutionized our attitude to sex toys.
- **Men no longer see vibrators as threatening but helpful.** There is no doubt (was there ever?) that vibrators help women orgasm, given that 60 per cent of women use them regularly. Men have finally caught on that vibrators can save him (and her) a hell of a lot of time and effort if he's too tired to lick or stroke her for the required amount of time.

The absolute essential for her

Every woman needs a couple of vibrators. One that will deliver an orgasm on demand, quickly, quietly, and efficiently and others for variety. Plenty to choose from.

- **Lots of women opt for a rabbit** as their mainstay (though I think you can do better). They're designed for penetration, while the little "ears" simultaneously vibrate on your clitoris, but since most girls just turn them around and use the ears, those fancy beads that whirl and twirl in the shaft are usually wasted.
- **If you like really strong vibration,** opt for an electric vibrator like the Hitachi Magic Wand that plugs into the power main (no, you won't be electrocuted, otherwise half the women in New York would be in their graves rather than running around with smiles on their faces).
- **Bullet vibes** are the size and shape of a tampon, provide surprisingly strong clitoral stimulation, are great for travel, and don't look like vibes if you have nosey flatmates or children.
- **Contour vibes** are small, oval shaped, and curved to cover the labial area. They'll suit you if you have a sensitive clitoris because the vibration is gentler.
- **U-shaped rocking vibrators** provide penetration, G-spot, and clitoral stimulation – all at the same time. I think they're a bit scary, quite frankly, but lots of women love them. Insert one end and aim towards the G-spot; the other, ridged end sits close to the clitoris with both ends vibrating. You then rock it back and forth using your palm.

He'll love...

- **A masturbatory sleeve.** Yes, I am talking a version of a "fake vagina" but before you both go "*Ewwww!*" and run away, hear me out. I was given a few samples of the new versions – jelly-like cylinders with soft "spikes" inside (picture a hairbrush without the wooden bit, turned inside out) – to see if I wanted to include them in my range of toys. My first reaction was to laugh. The second was to use them like stress balls because you can't help but pick them up and play with them. My then boyfriend's reaction was also to scoff. Until I insisted he let me try one on him and

then (smartass!) how quickly did he convert! I then lent samples to five of my most cynical male friends and the verdict was unanimous – you are so never getting them back! So check out the new saucy versions of "sex sleeves" and you'll find brilliantly versatile boy toys you can use solo or she can use on you. You simply put a dab of lube inside, slide them over the penis, and either use one hand to slide it up and down or hold one hand at the base for a different effect.

Stock up the toy chest

- **The basics:** condoms, lube (flavoured, silicone, and heavy-duty for anal), scarves and stockings for blind-folds and tie-ups, gorgeous lingerie (slutty and sweet), erotic magazines and DVDs, massage oils, candles.
- **Comfy handcuffs** if you love bondage.
- **Dress-up outfits** if you're into role-play.
- **Vibes to hold** on her clitoris during penetration or to add an extra buzz (sorry, couldn't resist) to oral sex.

Finger vibes are versatile and great for nipples, clitorises, and around the outside of bottom openings. Also invest in what's called a "classic vibe" – the old-fashioned style: a simple, slim cylinder. They're a good size to hang on to but not so big as to be intrusive between the two of you.

- **Whips and riding crops.** Rubber whips look fierce but are incredibly soft, giving a satisfying swish but landing like a kiss. If you want more, choose one made from soft, light leather. Riding crops make a more sinister slapping sound, which adds to the naughtiness, but again, they don't actually hurt.
- **Love eggs.** Slip these smooth, super-effective egg-shaped vibrators inside her for deliciously discreet vibrations. Double the pleasure by using fingers (or his tongue) simultaneously on the clitoris. Men love watching things disappear inside women – and not just his penis! Let him insert the egg and take control of the vibrations, as you lie back and enjoy electrifying oral sex. You can also buy eggs with remote controls if you want to play silly buggers in public.

Worth every penny

- **Vibrating penis rings.** Often rubber, these slide over an erect penis where they sit snugly at the base. Position the little vibrator so it makes contact with the clitoris once you've penetrated, then use a grinding, circular motion to maintain pressure. Good-quality rings really do up her chances of climaxing during penetration.
- **Pelvic-floor toners.** These are a good idea post-pregnancy or if you're worried you're not tight enough. You don't need a toner to do Kegel exercises but leaving one where you can see it might make you feel guilty enough to actually do them! Toners tend to either look like a set of kitchen tongs that you squeeze shut with your vaginal muscles or like little barbells that you squeeze against.
- **Hands-free "intercourse" vibes.** At the time of writing, the We-Vibe, a vibe you insert and leave in during intercourse, was selling so fast, the manufacturers could hardly keep up with demand. I love them – though I have to say, the

vote isn't unanimous. Insert the slender end of the C-shaped vibe into the vagina and it magically opens into an "L" shape with the clitoral pad ending up against the clitoris. He then penetrates. The bit that's inserted is just the right shape to stimulate the G-spot and both ends vibrate so you've got vibration on your clitoris and front vaginal wall as well as penetrative stimulation as his penis moves in and out. Few men can feel it, those that do say it's not unpleasant. Another hands-free option is to try a vibe that sits on top of the clitoris, held in place by straps that go around both her legs. The most famous is the butterfly, so named because the vibe sits inside a jelly "butterfly". These vibes never really flew off the shelves (oops, another pun!) probably because women felt a bit silly wearing the harness. Worth a whirl if you (wisely) don't care.
- **Glass dildos.** They look beautiful, feel fantastic, and are brilliant for both massage (roll them over the fleshy bits) and insertion. Nearly all are made from toughened glass so they won't break.

Have Just-Met Sex Tonight

Sex in the beginning is hot, frantic, and fuelled by lust rather than ruined by domesticity. Want it back again? The trick to recapturing that fresh excitement is to create sex scenarios that push you both firmly out of your comfort zones and back into treating each other like good old-fashioned sex objects. Just like you used to at the start, remember?

Here you'll find a list of simple, easy-to-do, relatively prop-free sex treats you can do for each other or together to shift your sex life up a gear. Or two. Or ten. They start out mild and climb higher on the sauciness scale as they go but I honestly don't think there's anything terribly outlandish or kinky in there. Certainly, there might be stuff you haven't done (I hope so, anyway!), which will raise your anxiety level. But that's a good thing – a bit of nervous excitement isn't going to harm either of you!

If you're conservative, a *lot* of what's on the list may *appear* completely outrageous to you. It's not. Be reassured that all of this stuff is what your average, healthy, well-adjusted, sexually satisfied couple get up to when no one's looking. I'm not talking other bodies in the bed. I'm not talking swingers' clubs. I'm not even talking swinging from chandeliers. You *can* do everything on this list.

Be adventurous! Playful. Daring. All the things you'd like to think you are (but maybe aren't so much, if you're really honest).

Having said that, as with anything I suggest, don't try anything you really are morally opposed to. But please push yourselves a little. Be adventurous! Playful. Daring. All the things you'd like to think you are (but maybe aren't so much, if you're really honest). At first, you'll feel self-conscious stepping outside that slippers-by-the-fire sexual comfort zone you've been existing in. But you'll get braver and bolder as you go along and when you're ready for a new challenge, get hold of one of my other books (*supersex*, *superhotsex*, *Sextasy* for starters) which are packed with practical suggestions. But we're getting ahead of ourselves. Enough chat, take a deep breath (and maybe a big gulp of wine), and let's get you started.

Easy-peasy starters

- **Have sex with your eyes open.** Seventy per cent of couples have sex with their eyes closed and only 15 per cent open them during orgasm, according to US author David Schnarch. "Most of us tune out our partner at a time that's supposed to be the most intimate," he says. Make eye contact all the way through. You'll laugh, you might even cry (some people do!) but you sure as hell will feel more connected.
- **Run a bubble bath** for her, fetch two glasses of champers, then jump right in there.
- **Sleep naked** – always. But especially if you're going through a low- or no-sex period. Skin-to-skin snuggling at least satisfies the cuddle craving.
- **Play in public.** Discreetly suck his finger like it's a small penis. Pull her palm to your mouth and bury your tongue in it.
- **Wake him up** at the weekend by putting his sleepy or erect penis in your mouth.
- **Park the car** and have sex in the garage.
- **Innocently chat to him while he's in the shower.** Then say, "God, your body turns me on." Quickly remove your clothes, and step in to give him a hand-job using a soapy, thick washcloth. Both the texture of the cloth and the spontaneity of the gesture guarantees you won't have to worry about your make-up running. It'll all be over in a flash!
- **Mix it up *every single time*.** Change one of the following elements for each session you have: the

time of day you do it, what room you do it in, what you're wearing, what position you choose, who initiates, what the focus of the session is (hand-job, oral, intercourse, etc).

- **Offer "no-strings" sex.** They don't have to do anything but lie back and take, take, take. (How nice does *that* sound? Let's face it, we're all selfish little buggers on the quiet.) Not only will this make you look wonderfully generous sexually, only the most selfish of partners won't feel obligated to return the favour at a later date.

Now you've got the idea...

- **Dare to do the clichés** like chocolate body paint poured on and licked off. The reason why they're clichés is because they're often what people want to do, but are too scared to.
- **Start a "sex jar".** Another golden oldie that works a treat. Each write down 10 things you'd like to try. Rip into separate points, fold, and put all of them into a jar. Pick out one a week to try. (Insist on pre-approval

All hail the vibrator

If there's one thing that defines whether a man is truly sexually confident, it's his comfort level with her vibrator. The guy who reaches into the bedside drawer and pulls one out to use on her during a hand-job, oral, or intercourse makes both her clitoris and heart swell with delight. It's not cheating to use a vibrator to ensure she has a guaranteed orgasm (just like he does most times), it's sensible and considerate. Official stats say vibrators are used by 21 per cent of the population worldwide – with the numbers increasing with age. Personally, I think those numbers aren't reflective – I'd put them way, way higher. If you're a man who's *really* out to impress with presents, ditch the predictable chocolates and flowers for a really stylish vibrator. She'll think you're the best thing since man invented hair straighteners. (Well, maybe not, but you'll come close!)

before you pop them in if you think "Lure the hot 18-year-old neighbour in for a threesome" will simply be repeated 10 times by your partner.)

Send sex texts. "I've been thinking about you inside me all day." "If you want it right now, I'm in the upstairs bedroom." "Remember when we did it on the beach? The kids are asleep…" Or, when you're feeling particularly horny (and they seem like they'd be receptive), "I want you to fuck me. Hard."

Shave each other's bits. It's a laugh… and sexier than you think!

Have a bed picnic. I think I include this in every single sex book I write! Not because I'm a lazy sod and can't think of anything new but because everyone tells me they love doing it! Jump into bed (or on the sofa) in sexy underwear and surround yourselves with goodies like champers, chocolates, strawberries, and other favourite yummies. Put a sexy DVD on the telly and half watch it as you loll around flicking through some sex books. Show each other things that take your fancy and use sticky notes to mark those you want to try later. If you're shy, read separately, then swap books, adding a different coloured sticky on things you agree to.

Shop for sex toys online. Read pages 162–4 to get an idea of what tickles your fancy and page 191 for good websites to cruise.

Wrap yourself as a present. Coloured non-stick bondage tape (available online) can be wrapped and fashioned into quite a cool boob tube and matching mini. Or grab the cling-film from the kitchen and wind around and around to encase your breasts. He can lick through it and unwrap you, layer by layer.

Try the "Kivin method". Transform a predictable oral sex session for her from dreary to dynamite with one slick move. Also called "Tahitian cunnilingus", you simply position your head at right angles to her body. You're licking up and down but because your head is perpendicular to her body, your tongue travels from side to side, producing an entirely new sensation. Place two fingers either side of the hood of the clitoris then slowly run your tongue back and forth and over and under the hood. Put the flat of your thumb on her perineum (the smooth bit between her bottom and vagina) and press firmly. Increase the speed the more

Play with each other on a plane. It's easier to get away with than you think if you cover yourselves with the blanket and choose a time when everyone else is sleeping or engrossed in the movie.

Go on, you know you want to

- **Have phone sex…** from the other room. Call her and tell her she has to do exactly what you say. Get her to go to the bedroom, take off her clothes, fondle her own breasts, lie down on the bed, start masturbating herself. Then walk in to finish the job.
- **Play stalker.** Lead him into a dark room, take off his shirt, then tie his hands behind his back with his tie before stripping him stark naked. You remain clothed. Stand behind him and tell him you've been watching him from across the road with binoculars.

Believe you're hot

Forget traffic-stopping breasts, swoon-worthy biceps; forget 300 notches on the bedpost, satin sheets, sex swings, a vice-tight vagina, or membership of the 10-inch club, nothing – and I mean *nothing* – is going to get you further in bed than confidence. It goes an awfully, awfully long way. Technique might be important but it's how you deliver it that's crucial. Scaredy-cat, tentative, "Is that OK?"-every-three-minutes-type lovers make the other person nervous. And if confidence is the sexiest thing both of you can take to bed, anxiety is the equivalent of wearing grey, baggy pants. This means trying out that new move with the self-assurance that if it goes wrong, you'll both just laugh it off. It means being open to new things, up for anything, and having enough self-belief to think you're pretty damn OK in the sack. It also means boosting your partner's sexual confidence by encouraging rather than criticizing, never making unfair comparisons, and being generally nice. Kindness is an underrated quality in sex. Yet the kinder you are to your lover, the more adventurous they'll be.

If confidence is the sexiest
thing both of you can
take to bed, anxiety is the
equivalent of wearing
grey, baggy pants.

Watch telly dressed for sex

Listen, I like slobby clothes just as much as the next girl but there's a limit to how often you can both pull on the same old moth-eaten sweatshirts and pants. Happily, there's a way to be super-comfy and sexy at the same time. Fine, for instance, for her to pull on a baggy singlet vest if there's a hot-coloured push-up bra peeking out underneath it. Fine also for him to pull on track pants, so long as they're low-rise and reasonably flattering around the bum, rather than saggy, egg-stained numbers. Yes, I know, you shouldn't have to look your best all the time but don't go to the other extreme. Even if you're staying in, pulling on a nice pair of jeans and top won't kill either of you.

You've dreamed of the day you could actually touch him and – what luck! – now he's virtually your sex slave. Do what you would do if this was true.

- **Make friends with his porn.** Most men watch porn. Fact. You might not like it, but it's going to happen anyway so if you can't beat it, join him. Go online solo and google "free porn" and you'll see a dazzling array of sites to choose from. Sample a variety to see what's out there and what all the fuss is about. Be amused, disgusted… turned on (come on, there's got to be something on there that puts a little twinkle in your eye!) Find something you find arousing, then when he gets home, put a beer in one hand, take him by the other and show him what you found. If you embrace his secret explorations rather than ban them, you could well have discovered a great way to

"kink" things up a bit – safely. (On that topic, let me clarify this just a little. First up, there's porn and there's porn. I'm talking the bog-standard stuff. Secondly, I honestly wouldn't recommend you go the whole hog and perform in front of a webcam. Unless you're really into that sort of thing, it's usually disastrous.) By the way, if you think other women don't indulge in such things as porn, you're wrong. A recent study in the US showed one in three visitors to adult porn sites in the first three months of 2007 was a woman. During the same period, nearly 13 million American women were checking out porn online at least once a month. Candida Royalle's erotic films, made expressly for women, sell more than 10,000 copies a month. And it's not *him* handing over the cashola for them – unless he's buying them

Get out of the house

Home might be where the heart is but it's also where the washing, kid's homework, and dreaded Sunday lunch with the in-laws is. US author Pamela Lister puts forward an interesting idea. "If once you put the kids to bed, you could both suddenly find yourself sitting at a gorgeous beach, being served fresh lobster and cocktails by a waiter – even if just for two hours – arguments would be cut to nil." Damn right. Tragically, unless you're Carrie Bradshaw and hooked up with Big (and live inside a telly) real life doesn't often deliver divine little time-outs like that. So it's up to you two to create some, even if it's to sit outside and look at the stars for 10 minutes. Make little bubbles of escape in your otherwise stressful lives.

or her! (If you're female and hate most porn, these ideas are well worth giving a go, by the way. Think of it as foreplay!)

Masturbate in front of each other. Come on! You've read this advice a hundred times before but avoided doing it out of embarrassment/prudishness/whatever. Thing is, you will learn so much about each other by doing this, I bloody well insist you at least give it a try! If you're really shy, close your eyes so you can't see them watching. Even if you don't actually masturbate with your fingers anymore (why would you when a vibrator does the job *sooooo* well for you?), pretending to do it is enough. Men are generally less shy about showing off but don't launch into it so quickly that she doesn't get to see what technique, grip, and hold you use. This isn't just a turn-on exercise, it's a show-and-tell one.

Play "What if you could do anything you want?" It's a fantasy game. Ask them "What's the thing you'd most like to do in bed that would surprise me? Then... I'll tell you." If they're shy, you start. Make it silly or funny to begin with and if they claim there's nothing they'd like to do that they haven't already done, tell them to make something up. Believe me, people *always* have something up their sleeve (or other less savoury parts). Letting them pretend it's "made up" let's them put something out there and see your reaction without risking anything. If it's "I'd rather scoop my eyes out with a teaspoon" all they have to do is say, "Well, you said to make anything up!" Sneaky or what! The more you share, the more they'll share. Give examples to establish parameters, so they know how far they can go (a relatively tame 'I'd like to tie you up" to "I'd love you to pretend I'm a hooker/pretend you're with a hooker").

Plan more adventures. You've done all of these already? Well, well, well. And there's you thinking you were too shy to even finish the starters... A little effort can give you orgasms galore in return!

Forget traffic-stopping breasts or membership of the 10-inch club, nothing will get you further in bed than confidence.

Play to their dirty little secret

All of us have a core erotic theme: something we need to express to be able to fuel or feel desire. On a simple level it might be having sex in public, a penchant for wearing slutty clothes or thigh-high boots, "pretend" rape, sex with more than one person, being spanked or anally penetrated. It's a spin-off of our erotic blueprints (see page 26). Most of us find a way to indulge our core erotic themes on a level we feel comfortable with. That might be through a fantasy we play in our heads during masturbation. Or by watching a certain type of porn, or through role-play – or real play, if we take it through to real life.

A lot of people guard their core erotic themes fiercely from their partners, especially if they consider them even slightly "dodgy", for fear of offending or losing them. But even if *they* won't tell, that doesn't stop you snooping! You'll usually get at least a sense of their theme, the more you explore sex together. Once you feel instinctively that you've "got" your partner's "naughty secret", indulge them without *ever* actually saying a word.

You've figured if he loves taking you from behind, holding your wrists together, and pulling your hair, he's got a bit of a secret "rape" fantasy going on? You're probably right. (This is common, by the way, and in 99 per cent of cases does *not* mean you're in danger or will have the police knocking at the door.) Indulge it by either "pretend fighting" or putting up zero resistance when you're having sex. (You can't ask outright what the women in his fantasy would do, so play to both scenarios.) She's given vague hints that she fantasizes about having sex with a woman, even though she hasn't dared (or doesn't want to) take it through to reality? Pop some "lipstick lesbian" porn in the DVD player, pretend it's what you fancy watching, and see how she reacts. Indulge each other's core erotic theme and *you* satisfy both your core erotic selves. The ultimate!

What I've learnt so far...

To go back to sex school by checking my technique is up to scratch so I can deliver deliciously new sensations rather than the same tired old stuff.

To correct any bad sex habits that may have been driving my partner quietly insane for the last 10 years.

To try one new thing once a week for the next two months from all the ideas in this chapter (and book). We'll take it in turns to choose.

To be brave and adventurous and not crinkle my nose up at anything daring my partner suggests that I don't fancy.

To believe my partner thinks I'm both attractive and desirable, rather than secretly critical of the not-so-hot bits.

To have sex out of the house as often as possible. Even if it means kicking the kids out of the tent in the back garden.

6
Lust That Lasts

Love You Long Time

The crucial ingredients you need to survive the storm, keep you in a happy place, prevent a relapse, and guide you through, should you need to (gulp!) call in the professionals.

Well, congratulations! Assuming you haven't started the book backwards, you've just been on one hell of a journey. I'm desperately hoping it wasn't too bumpy a ride, that it was bloody enjoyable in (lots of) parts, and that the end destination is what you were hoping for: Planet Happy and Satisfied! By all means find that bottle of special champagne you've been saving for a moment like this, down the lot, and end up in a messy, happy heap, sniggering on the sofa. But just as that delicious, fuzzy buzz will disappear by the morning once the alcohol's worn off, so too will the emotional high you're riding right now.

It's very common for couples – especially those who've dragged themselves back from the jaws of separation or divorce – to think this new-found, sexual euphoria will last forever. Truth is, it probably (most definitely, to be honest, but don't hate me for saying it) won't. When that happens – you have a fight or slip back into old habits momentarily and occasionally – please don't make the mistake of throwing your hands up and thinking all is lost. You *are* going to have arguments, you *are* going to have "Nothing's changed at all!" moments. It's normal and usually harmless. It's having unrealistic expectations that is more harmful.

Lots of experts say the true test of a good relationship isn't how many problems the couple have but how quickly and effectively they recover from them. Relationships aren't constant. They dip up and down – and it's the same with sex. Sometimes we want it, sometimes we don't. Penises go limp, breasts get tender, orgasms happen too fast, too slow, or not at all, sometimes. So try really hard not to overreact to things. If something happens, don't snap straight into panic mode. Either ignore it and wait

for a bit, laugh it off, or talk it through in a light manner. Don't blame, accuse, or stress, and chances are it will be a lapse not a relapse. You fixed it last time, you can fix it again. You've now got the skills and knowledge to get on track quickly. All you need now is a little reassurance… and a maintenance plan, which is rather handily set out for you below.

Then there are those of you who have faithfully followed the course all the way through and still come out the other side troubled and dissatisfied. This could mean you need professional help. Or it could mean you lacked the necessary prerequisites for the process to work. Check the "What you need to succeed" section first and see if there's something obviously lacking there. If there is and you can fix it, do it, and try again. If there isn't, call in the experts and see the section on "Getting help". There are *very* few relationships, where both people genuinely want it to work, that can't be saved. I'll offer a bet, yours isn't one of them.

What you need to succeed

Studies show the couples that are most likely to survive rough patches have most or all of the following:

The obvious: energy, patience, sensitivity. And a smattering of love on both sides wouldn't go astray.

Motivation: if either of you has already emotionally left the relationship and doesn't *want* to make it work, nothing you do is going to work. (There are, however, good arguments for trying anyway and especially for going to couple counselling: you might change your mind, you'll leave knowing you tried your best, and you will have left your partner in good hands that can help if/when you leave.)

Commitment: if you know you're both genuinely committed to sorting things out and don't have secret "deadlines" (I'll wait till the kids grow up then leave), you'll be able to let go of the anxiety and paranoia that can stop you seeing things clearly.

Time: fixing your sex and love life must be top of both your priority lists. You must both be willing to make time to do whatever it takes to get things back in shape and moving forwards again.

The willingness to change: if you're not prepared to make any changes, you're effectively saying you are perfect exactly how you are and it's your partner who has to do all the changing. Get real. *No one's* that great, honey. No, not even you.

Accepting you need to compromise: new couples tend to have one of two reactions when they hear about compromises made by couples who've been together forever: "We won't have to because we're different" or "If I end up having to do that, I am so outta here". Truth is, there is no such thing as an ideal relationship. Everyone compromises. You let go of the tooth fairy. Now let go of this.

Wanting to end the war: if you're trapped in a bitter stand-off with each of you unwilling to make the first move to extend an olive branch, you're locked in there for life. Do you want to be right or be happy?

The courage to open up: if you really want a close, loving relationship that's relatively free of problems, you have to let people get close to you. That means opening up completely – laying yourself naked in *every* sense. This is scary and some people can't handle it. They feel panicky and overwhelmed by the intimacy, and sabotage it or run away.

Wanting to understand more than be understood: we all want to feel like we matter, our feelings matter, and that our partners care deeply about us. Thing is, if you don't feel cherished, it's highly unlikely you're going to make your partner feel loved. "You can't open your arms to your lover if they're folded across your chest protecting you," says US therapist Dr Sandra Scantling. It's a vicious catch-22. Neither of you is budging because you don't feel understood but if neither budges you never will be. If you seek to *understand* rather than to be *understood*, you will get a lot further. One of you has to be gracious. Why not let it be you?

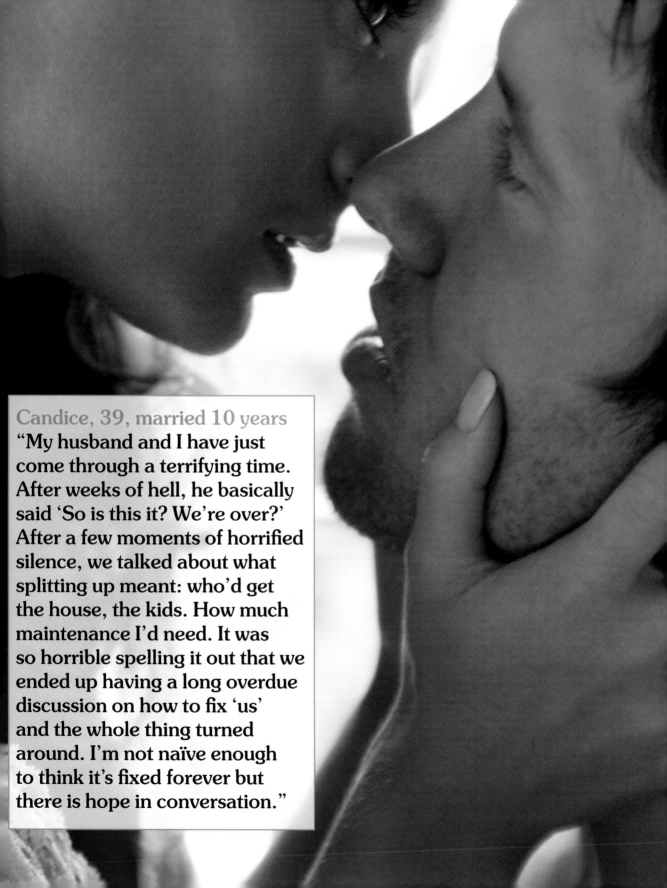

Candice, 39, married 10 years
"My husband and I have just come through a terrifying time. After weeks of hell, he basically said 'So is this it? We're over?' After a few moments of horrified silence, we talked about what splitting up meant: who'd get the house, the kids. How much maintenance I'd need. It was so horrible spelling it out that we ended up having a long overdue discussion on how to fix 'us' and the whole thing turned around. I'm not naïve enough to think it's fixed forever but there is hope in conversation."

01

Laugh as often as possible. Play, be silly, use humour to diffuse potentially volatile situations. It's infectious and therapeutic!

02

Share everything that happens to you, especially the little things. Let your partner in on how your life is affecting you.

03

Argue. You're far better off having a row, where you both get every-thing off your chest, than keeping it all inside.

04

Give. Be generous with your time, affection, body, everything! Make each other the most important people in your world.

Good health: a lot of emotional and sexual problems can be directly linked to physical problems, lifestyle choices, and medication. Get these fixed. Visit your GP for a health check-up or to discuss any specific problems.

How to stay sorted

Here, a maintenance plan to prevent – or deal with – any relapses:

Keep up the good work – daily. You've both learnt new ways to behave and it's transformed your sex life and/or relationship. Congratulations! Now you have to *keep* on doing whatever it is that's working, *every single day*. The brain likes doing what's familiar because it requires the least effort. It will be trying it's damnedest to make you slip back into old habits, no matter how destructive they were. Fight this by consciously practising your new "habits" so they will eventually replace the old. Experts say it takes a minimum of six weeks for this to happen. I believe it takes a good three to six months.

Do nice things regularly, not just on special occasions. A weekend away works wonders but the high can't last forever. Make sure you're continually planning a healthy slab of fun and pleasure – both inside and outside the bedroom – to balance out the inevitable stress and daily chores.

Do new things weekly. Go to places you haven't been before. Have sex there. Do things you haven't done before. In bed, out of bed. You get the theme…

Don't lose the "you time" you found. If you had therapy on a regular basis, you both managed to clear your diaries for a couple of hours a week. You did it before, keep doing it. Use that time to have sex, do something nice together, or talk through any problems.

Pinpoint the warning signs you got last time around. How will you know if it's happening again? Work out what first alerted you both that things were

Work out what rescued you

Sound advice from the *ever-practical therapist Michele Weiner Davis*: have a plan of action if it happens again, based on what worked last time round. What was the pivotal point when the lightbulbs went on? Which techniques worked, which didn't? What were you both doing/saying or not doing/saying that made the difference? The more accurately you can pin it down, the better chance you have of blitzing any future relapses before they blow up. What were your strengths, your partner's strengths? What were both your weaknesses? Give each other "jobs" to keep an eye on different things. Write this all down, in detail, and keep it.

going off the rails. It might be spending more time apart, not cuddling at night. It might be having sex less frequently, erection problems, not being able to orgasm, one of you not initiating sex anymore. Make a list and be as specific as possible.

Set new goals every month if your relationship needed a lot of fixing and is still a work in progress. Make sure you also give yourselves time off if you're both exhausted from constantly working on the relationship. Call an official "time-out" for a couple of days or a week where all talk about the relationship is banned – along with arguments. Just be nice to each other while you catch your breath.

Have some type of formal meeting every six months. It could be with your therapist or just a time when you sit down together and be honest about where you're at, award gold stars, and check all is well.

Swing into action if needed: If you honestly think you're heading back to where you were, admit you're worried, check in with each other, and talk about whether you both agree it's something to take notice of. Now's the time for those lists you made: look at them and do what you did last time that worked. (The proactive stuff, not the long discussions, unless the problem is something new.) Give it three weeks and see if there's improvement. It's solved itself again? Fanbloodytastic! If it hasn't and you haven't before, call in the professionals. If you've already been to therapy, now's the time for a top-up.

Getting help

Most couples turn to professionals like sex therapists, therapists, counsellors, psychotherapists, psychologists, or psychiatrists when they've exhausted every other alternative. And I mean every alternative. Not only will you suck your friends dry for advice, read every book printed on the topic, clock up 560 hours on the internet, compulsively check your horoscopes and have your palms read, you might even try mixing strands of hair with powdered goat testicles and a drop of your own blood. All in a desperate bid to avoid doing what everyone dreads: going for couple counselling. In the UK at least, admitting you need help with your relationship and seeing "someone" is tantamount to saying you're on the brink of divorce. Sadly, this is usually true since most couples wait an average of seven years before they turn to a professional to help them save a troubled relationship. Silly, silly, *silly!* Had you gone at the first sign of real trouble, not only could you have saved yourselves the following miserable years (perhaps even decades), it's a lot easier to fix problems when the couple isn't in crisis (either having an affair or about to walk out the door). I'm not saying it's not worth going if you have left it a long (long) time – it is. But I am saying you're much better off going sooner (like now) rather than later. Eighty per cent of people who go to therapy end up better off mentally, physically, and emotionally than those who receive no treatment. They're pretty good odds.

Having been on both ends of couple counselling, I can tell you, hand on heart, that it's not even a fraction as bad as you think it's going to be. In fact, it's not so much getting couples to keep coming once they start counselling that's the problem, it's getting them to stop. Think about it. No matter what happens in your week, if you're having weekly counselling, you *know* it's going to be dealt with at 6pm on Thursday night (or whenever). That's reassuring. If your partner does or says something hurtful, instead of reacting, you gleefully think "Wait till I tell the counsellor *that* little gem!" You get to talk about yourselves without feeling guilty, bring up stuff you wouldn't dare tackle alone, drop your partner in it at *every* opportunity, *and* have an independent adjudicator a finger snap away when you're desperate to be proven right! Of course, your partner's thinking and doing exactly the same thing you are, so it's not all fun and games. But there's a reason why Americans are addicted to therapy: nothing is more interesting than a conversation about yourself!

Having lured you in with all the fun stuff, I'm not going to pretend it's not hard work, emotionally painful, and quite horrid at times. Some days you'll walk out of there with a skip in your step that's been missing for years. Other times, you'll be crying so hard you can't even see the door. Most times, you'll walk out with your

head spinning with information overload mixed with a cautious degree of hope. All three reactions are part of the healing process but if you allow yourselves to go with the flow and choose a therapist wisely, the results can be nothing short of spectacular.

I've convinced you but your partner refuses to consider the idea? Go solo. It will help you and it will show your partner you're serious about fixing the two of you. If they see you're not just surviving but thriving, they might change their mind. Check with the therapist on whether you should give your partner feedback on what you're talking about but do let them know it's not as bad as they think and they're welcome to join you at any point.

Choosing the right therapist

There are different types of therapists to suit your specific problems. If you or your partner feel particularly mixed up or there's something specific in either of your pasts like abuse, rape, trust issues, or a particularly difficult childhood, it might be worth doing some work solo before tackling it together. (If you know the issue, see a therapist who is experienced in that area.) If you think it's more a relationship issue, choose a therapist that's experienced in and specializes in couple counselling. It's a completely different ball game

counselling two people rather than one, involving different skills. The focus isn't on personal growth but relationship growth. The therapist has to figure you out, then your partner, make you both feel heard, observe your dynamics, and identify and sort out your problems without ever making either of you feel they've taken sides. Not easy.

If your problem seems to be specifically about sex, you need to see a sex therapist or a therapist, psychologist, or psychiatrist who specializes in sex problems. Don't go to someone who lumps sex into a whole list of things they'll tackle. You want an expert in the area. If it's something to do with physical performance or a technique problem like trouble achieving orgasm, ejaculation issues, pain during intercourse, or similar, you're better off with a sex therapist. If sex is a problem but it's more "feelings" based, choose a psychologist or psychiatrist who specializes in sex. For desire problems, take your pick of the two.

Get a personal recommendation or, otherwise, *always* check a therapist's credentials and qualifications and ask if they belong to an association and are accredited – especially if you're going with an individual rather than a reputable organization. Lots of people call themselves therapists or counsellors without any qualifications, so be careful. Ask questions. Ask what qualifications they have, how long they've been practising. Ask if they specialize in any particular area

to get an idea of what they're truly passionate about and ask about their theoretical approach. If they start spouting psychobabble, ask them to explain it in layman's terms. They should be able to do this easily – if they can't talk in a language you understand, they'll be unable to explain other skills and concepts you may need to know. Briefly tell them your problem and ask for an idea of how many sessions it will take, and how often they'd want to see you. Then find out their fees (some offer reduced fees in special circumstances).

Before you go

- **Ask to chat on the phone before making an appointment.** Ask questions, get to know them a bit, then make a shortlist of two. Make an appointment with both, checking they have time to take you on, at a convenient time, if you want to see them regularly.

- **Work out what you want from the sessions.** The better read you are, the less they have to "teach" you. The more specific your goals and problems, the better they'll know where to start. They might not agree with what you think the problems are but it's certainly a good place to start.

- **Find out their style of therapy.** Most therapists will listen more than they'll talk and prefer to guide you to a point where *you* come up with the solutions or pinpoint problems. But if you want more advice and interaction, tell them. Ask if they're happy doing this.

- **Check the therapist is goal-orientated**. Tell them what your goals are and ask outright if they can help and how long they expect it will take.

Once you're there

- **You should feel respected, heard, and listened to.** It's also crucial the therapist doesn't take sides.

- **The focus should be on telling you what will work or is working,** rather than what isn't. I once went to a couple counsellor and she said "You're both clearly hanging by a thread." It wasn't helpful. While we desperately loved each other, constant arguments were ruining us. We didn't need her to tell us we were on the verge of splitting up, that's why we were there! Had she said, "You both clearly love each other. I'm sure we can work this out" and asked for positive reasons why we wanted to stay together rather than focusing on our unhappiness, it may have worked. The therapist isn't God. If you don't like what they're saying, stick up for yourselves or find someone new.

- **Speak up if you're not happy.** It's normal to feel uncomfortable and even to briefly detest your therapist if they make you admit to things that perhaps *are* your fault. But you should see the point of it. If you don't, ask why. If you don't like the style of therapy or it doesn't suit, ask them to try an alternative approach. You should feel comfortable, trust, and like the therapist, and roughly share the same values and goals.

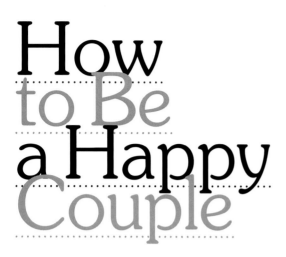

How to Be a Happy Couple

Don't try to control each other. They aren't you and you aren't them so stop trying to turn them into you by controlling what they do or trying to influence how they think.

Don't take everything personally. Your partner's behaving like a right so-and-so? It could be they just got off the phone from their mother having a rant or they're worried about money – and don't feel like discussing either with you. You're not the only person and thing influencing your partner's moods.

Talk about the happy times. Especially when you're going through a rough patch. Remind yourselves of how good you are together when things are normal. It keeps things in perspective.

Do lots together, no matter how mundane. Whether it's the weekly shop, washing the dog, eating dinner on your laps in front of the telly, it all counts. Quality "you two" time is important but one "date" a week isn't going to beat spending time together frequently, no matter how routine it might be.

Watch your language. There's a reason why this is mentioned in every relationship article. Say "I feel this way" not "You made me feel this way." Don't make sweeping generalizations like "You never do this or that" or "You're always late."

Touch each other constantly. Both sexually and affectionately – and make sure you know the difference.

Know each other's "raw" spots. Be sensitive to vulnerabilities, rather than use them to score points. If your partner's down, be extra nice and they'll return the favour when you're not feeling so chipper.

Don't always assume the worst. He didn't make the effort to come and see your mum in hospital? She was late to an important work "do"? Instead of assuming they did it deliberately, ask why. Perhaps they didn't realize how important it was to you. Spell out your needs very clearly and don't expect your partner to read your mind.

Honesty isn't the best policy. To be 100 per cent honest, you would have to express every fleeting sexual thought you have about others and every negative thing you think about your partner. Neither is wise. Be tactful, be kind, and hold back the really nasty stuff you're desperate to blurt out in the middle of an argument.

Don't try to change the other person. Don't play the "if only" game. If only they were kinder, richer, happier, had more hair, or bigger breasts. We can't change other people. All we can change is our reaction to them.

Put yourself in your partner's shoes. Before you react defensively, see the problem from their point of view, through their eyes, and from their perspective. Then speak.

Don't do all the work in the relationship. If you're always the one who steps in to solve things, you don't give your partner the chance to try. You feel resentful for doing all the fixing, they feel controlled.

Treat your partner the way you treat your friends. We wouldn't dream of speaking to friends the way we do our partners. Have some manners.

Silence is deadly. Fine to shut up until you've calmed down but not speaking for days on end is incredibly damaging. The longer you don't get on, the bigger the argument has time to grow.

If you're tempted to start afresh, remember new lovers turn into old lovers. That shiny, new, fault-free relationship is going to develop its own bug-bears in time. Don't kid yourself otherwise.

Make your own rules. You're unique, so is your partner, and so is your relationship. People like me can rattle on all they want but only you two know what works for you.

Index

attitudes 59
initiating *see* initiating sex
making time for *see* time
naughty *see* naughty sex
new ideas/techniques
147–53
not always feeling like it 14
overinvolved couple 43–4
passionate couple 46
planning/scheduling 72, 84
practical couple 46
replacements 56
sex drive/desire/libido 101
faking desire 83
health problems and 59, 61
increased by sex 110–11
low/disappearing 12, 22,
31, 32, 56, 64, 74, 80,
86, 108–9, 118
man 93
mismatched (higher/lower)
12, 31, 59, 62, 81, 101,
118
sex games/scenarios 166–75
role-play 32, 91, 138, 164,
170, 174
"sex jar" 169–70
sex life/relationship
assessing yours 10–17
changes over time 28–37,
59
problems *see* sex problems
statistics 10, 16, 74
sex problems 51–9
relationship problems and,
which to solve first 81

signs of not having 12–14
sorting/solving 80–7,
134–42, 180–5
companionate couple 44
disconnected couple 42–3
healthy couple 49
over-involved couple 44
passionate couple 49
practical couple 46
sex styles/personalities 18–26
sex therapists 16, 19, 35, 80
sex toys 112, 162–4, 170
vibrators 114, 156, 162,
164, 169
sex worker fantasy 164
sexual intercourse
in affair 131
positions 154–6
sharing 182
shaving her legs 114
shopping
sex toy 170
underwear 114
showers 112, 139, 148,
156, 168
sleeping naked 72, 93, 168
sleepy sex 72, 156
solo, solving problems 139
solo sex/masturbation 12,
44, 49, 82
spanking 114, 159,
160
stabilizer personality 19, 21
stalker (role-play) 170
stress 56, 93
strip clubs 131

T

Tahitian cunnilingus 170
talking
about kids all the time 72
about sex and sex problems
16, 49, 80–1, 82, 95,
96, 102, 114, 134–43
with friends 96
listening and *see* listening
sexy 168
telephone sex 170
television (TV)
removing from bedroom
72
sex portrayed on 14
testicles 148, 150
texting 61, 114, 170
therapists 184–5
sex 16, 19, 35, 80
thighs, closed, penis thrusting
between 155
thrusting style 155
time
to change things/fix
problems 139, 180
changes in sex life over
28–37, 59
to climax 14
making time for sex 44, 84
not 61
spare, not wasting 72
taking time over sex 86
tiredness and exhaustion
56, 118
turn-ons *see* fantasies

U

U-shaped rocking vibrators 162
unattractiveness 55, 85
understanding each other 180
problems 59
underwear shopping 114
unfaithfulness (affairs and
infidelity) 56, 121, 125–33

V, W

vibrators 114, 156, 162, 164,
169
warm sex 73
We-Vibe 164
weight problems 55
whips 164
woman
exciting her 114
G-spot 162, 164
hand-job by *see* hand-job
hand-job on 152–3
hand-job on self during sex 14
initiating sex 62
intercourse makeover 154–5
no sex due to 29
not wanting sex 29, 98–105
oral sex by 119, 148
oral sex for 148–9, 170
orgasm *see* orgasm
worry and anxiety 22, 56,
137, 170

Thanks

This is my 13th book (but not really if you count the little pocket books – well, that's what I'm telling myself to avoid the curse!), so my friends and family are used to me disappearing off the face of the planet for months at a time. It also means the people I always thank for putting up with it and being generally fabulous and supportive are used to me waxing lyrical about them. (I bet you don't flick to the back and check anymore, do you? Or do you? Am tempted to miss someone out just to see!)

First thanks, as always, go to my family who I love and miss in equally gigantic proportions: my mother Shirley, father Patrick and his wife Maureen, my brother Nigel and his wife Diana, my sister Deborah and her husband Doug, and my niece and nephew Maddie and Charlie.

Vicki McIvor is my agent, best friend, and someone I couldn't and never want to live without. Vic, I think you are amazing, and Lara, my little god-daughter, continues to both look and behave like she's fallen from heaven.

I love all my friends desperately and wish I had the space here to tell each and every one of you why you are so special to me. But I don't, so I will simply name you in alphabetical order and hope you realize how much I appreciate you all: Sandra Aldridge, Diana Beaumont, Peggy Bunker, Matt Butterworth, Rachel Corcoran, Claire Faragher, Tracy and Hamo Forsyth (and my lovely Cosmo), James Foster, Steph Harris, Catherine Jarvie (and kisses to Jack), Justin Knott, Victoria Lehmann, Claire Merryweather, Jeremy Milnes, Kate Morey, Karen Reid, and Fenella Thomas. If I have forgotten anyone, please know it's because I am writing this very, very late at night, about 500 vodkas in, and it has to go to print first thing tomorrow.

My editor, Dawn Bates, deserves ultra-special thanks for working such long hours on this book and being consistently brilliant. I love all the staff at DK, world-wide, but special thanks on this one to Stephanie Jackson, Adèle Hayward, and Kat Mead. I have, again, no room to list you all! Thanks to Richard Longhurst and Neal Slateford at Love Honey, who produce my sex toy range, for providing sassy sex toys for the shoot and for continuing to be so wonderful to work with.

Finally, a heartfelt thank you to all the couples who so graciously agreed to be interviewed for the book and answered so honestly. Your help was immeasurable.

DK would like to thank Clare Hubbard for proofreading and Dr Laurence Errington for the index. A big thank you to Sara Robin, Katherine Raj, and Saskia Janssen for looking after the design with such meticulous care. DK gratefully acknowledges the following companies for loaning clothes and props for the photoshoot: Ann Summers, House of Harlot, Knickerbox, La Senza, Made by Niki, and www.mytights.com. Thank you to Peter Mallory for his casting and production expertise, Sarah Cromwell for art direction, and Calvin Bishop and Michael Protin for on-shoot assistance.

References

Sex toys: Check out my range (shameless plug here, sorry!) at www.traceycox.com or browse through the many beautiful toys for sale on www.lovehoney.co.uk, www.sh-womenstore.com, www.babeland.com, and www.edenfantasys.com

Therapy and counselling: In the UK, I'd recommend any of the following: The British Association for Counselling (www.bacp.co.uk) and British Association for Sexual and Relationship Therapy (www.basrt.org.uk). Both have excellent websites that will guide you through what to look for in a therapist, questions to ask, what will happen in a typical session, how many sessions it usually takes, how much it costs, and how to find one near you. Also check out the British Psychological Society site (www.bps.org.uk) and Relate, the UK's leading couple-counselling charity (www.relate.org.uk).